The SIG Handguns

By

Duncan Long

Edited by Larry Combs

Desert Publications

El Dorado, AR 71731-1751 U. S. A.

The SIG Handguns

Published by
Desert Publications
P.O. Box 1751
El Dorado, AR 71731-1751
501-862-2077

ISBN 0-87947-096-8
10 9 8 7 6 5 4 3 2 1
Printed in U. S. A.

Desert Publication is a division of
The DELTA GROUP, Ltd.
Direct all inquires & orders to the above address.

Acknowledgement

Thanks must go to Kevin Rowe of Sigarms, Inc., and Martin Mandall of Mandall Shooting Supplies as well as officials at the other companies listed in this book who supplied me with a wealth of photos, information, and sample products for the researching and writing of this book.

I must also thank Larry Combs for coming up with this book idea (though not entirely without ulterior motives since Larry is a big fan of the SIG-Sauer pistols); thanks should also go to Larry for again shaping one of my manuscripts into its final form through his editing and the "magic" he performs with scanner and computer. It once was a joke that photos would "look much better" when the printer was finished doing the book; now, thanks to Larry, many of the photos I submit along with my typo-plagued manuscripts really do look better in print.

And of course my usual gratitude must be expressed to Maggie, Kristen, and Nicholas for their help and patience.

Warning

Technical data presented here, particularly technical data on ammunition and the use, adjustment, and alteration of firearms, inevitably reflects the author's individual beliefs and experience with particular firearms, equipment, and components under specific circumstances which the reader cannot duplicate exactly. The information in this book should therefore be used for guidance only and approached with great caution. Neither the author nor the publisher assumes any responsibility for the use or misuse of information contained in this book.

Contents

Chapter 1
Starting in the Good Old Days

SIG (Schweizerische Industrie Gesellschaft, Neuhausen/ Rheinfalls, Switzerland) is an old company, tracing its origins back to 1853. As one might imagine with a firm that's been in business this long, SIG has established a reputation for high quality firearms, both from a design and reliability standpoint as well as through the fine finish and craftsmanship displayed with each firearm the enterprise produces.

The company has more or less specialized in military weapons, with its rifles, submachine guns, and machine guns supplying the Swiss military over the years with armies and police departments of other countries often purchasing limited numbers of these arms as well. Following World War I, SIG engineers branched out a bit and initiated work that eventually resulted in a series of semiauto pistols.

The potential market for such pistols had been slowly unfolding as the Swiss Army and many of the country's police forces became more and more dissatisfied with the Luger (Parabellum) pistol that had been adopted as the standard military pistol in 1900. Manufactured in Germany, the pistols were elegant but expensive. Too, they often proved to be somewhat sensitive to the type of ammunition being fired in them and the 7.62mm (.30 Luger) cartridge they were chambered for proved less than ideal in combat. Little wonder the

Swiss government initiated an effort to improve this situation shortly after the adoption of the Luger.

The first step toward improving the Swiss army's pistol situation involved revamping the Luger design; the end result was the slightly improved version designated the "1904." Improvements were only minor; these pistols were still virtually identical to the German design with only the extractor, firing pin, recoil spring, and a few secondary parts differing from the original design. The 1904 model was manufactured under license in Berne.

In 1929 another new model was introduced in an effort to reduce the cost of the pistols which required a lot of tooling to manufacture. This redesign work was carried out by Waffenfabrik Bern and the principal changes were the elimination of knurling on the cocking toggles, straightening of the front strap of the grip, and the use of plastic rather than wooden grip plates. But as one might imagine, these changes resulted in only minor reductions of cost and, when compared to German-made guns (fabricated with cheaper German labor), the "cheaper" Swiss design actually resulted in a pistol that was more expensive to manufacture at the government arsenal in Switzerland. Nevertheless the Swiss military decided to go with their slightly improved design that could be produced within the Swiss borders, preferring to have full control of their pistol supply rather than being dependant on Germany which was slowly sinking into chaos. But the situation was far from ideal.

The new model of the Swiss Luger, designated the "07/29", went into production in 1933. Around 27,900 of the pistols were manufactured before production was discontinued in 1947 with an additional 2,000 pistols being manufactured for commercial sales during this period.

Even from the time that the 07/29 was adopted, the Swiss military was dissatisfied with it; word was leaking out that it would be replaced when a suitable gun design appeared. Soon a number of companies were looking into the possibility of creating a replacement pistol for the Swiss military. One of these companies was SIG.

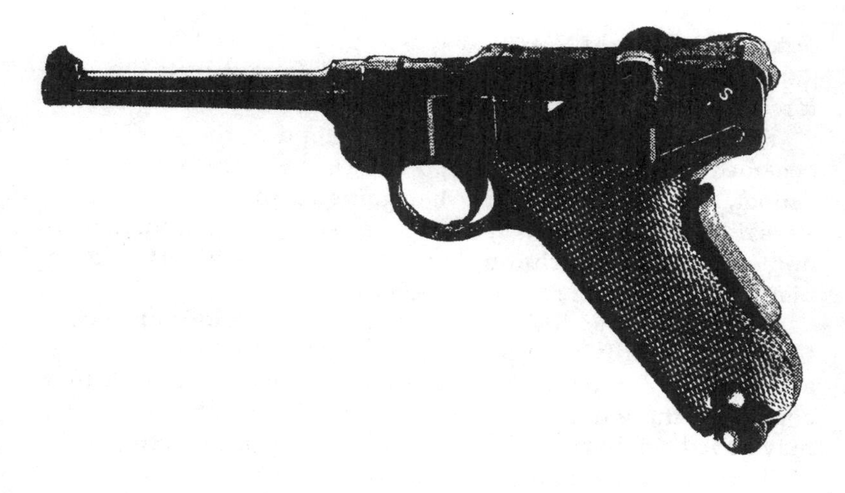

Swiss Luger 07/29

By this point in time, SIG had cut its teeth on the manufacture of a simple blow-back .25 ACP semiauto pistol and had been making parts for the Swiss army's Lugers as well. Gearing up to produce a new center-fire pistol was the next logical step for the company. Rather than start from scratch or try to adapt one of the company's rifle or submachine gun mechanisms to a pistol, SIG engineers decided instead to choose a promising pistol design as their starting point toward the creation of a new military pistol. This did away with a lot of design work up front, permitting the engineers to concentrate on improvement and reliability rather than work at creating and then perfecting an all-new firearm. The pistol SIG chose for their starting point was the French Pistol 35A which was being produced in France by SACM (Societe d'Applicatins Generales, Electriques et Mecaniques). In 1937, SIG purchased a license from SACM to manufacture and modify the patents which were owned by Charles Petter.

Petter had led a colorful life before becoming a firearms designer. Swiss by birth, Petter had served for a short time in the Swiss army as a training officer. From this position he moved to Belgium, working as a mining engineer until the outbreak of World War I, at which point he went to France, joined the French Foreign Legion, and fought until he was forced to retire because of a stomach wound received in battle.

Following his recuperation and the end of the war, Petter became the director of the weapons division of SACM. Based in Chloet, Alsace, an area France had gained through the Treaty of Versailles, SACM was responsible for several weapons development programs including the creating of a new self-loading pistol that was the brainchild of Petter.

Technically the design borrowed heavily from John Moses Browning, modifying Browning's swinging link lockup system and coupling it with an innovative removable module that contained the hammer assembly—though arguably this, too, may have been borrowed (from a Feodor Tokarev pistol). One of the few "innovations" on the pistol was a slide-mounted safety—an awkward device that was nearly impossible to operate easily. Nevertheless the overall design was sound and the pistol had eye-pleasing lines to it as well.

Petter actually produced two versions of his pistol. One was designated the "Modele 1935A" and had a conventional locking system; in 1938, the 1935S version of the gun was created; this design had a lug that locked into the ejection port (a design that would later be copied by SIG engineers). The Modele 1935S was less expensive to produce than was the 1935A and soon superseded it.

Unfortunately both the 1935A and 1935S were chambered for the French 7.65mm Long which the French Army was, for some odd reason, greatly enamored with, despite the fact that it was horribly ineffective, especially with the FMJ (Full Metal Jacket) bullets dictated by the conventions of war. Therefore the 1935A and 1935S were never noted for being effective combat weapons, despite the overall good design of the pistol. (Following WWII, the French military had the pistol redesigned to accept the 9mm Luger cartridge. This new pistol was designated the "Modele 1950" and is for the most part simply a revamped Modele 1935.)

SIG assembled the machinery to produce the Modele 1935A from 1938 through 1940, making a series of "Selbstladepistole

French 1935A

Petter" guns mostly for the purpose of testing variants on the basic firearm's design. Chambered for 7.65mm Luger, 7.65mm Longue, or 9mm Luger, these models were otherwise virtually identical to the French 1935A but did permit the Swiss engineers to perfect their tooling techniques and design skills to produce a highly reliable firearm. More importantly, perhaps, the tests also showed that the 9mm Luger was the best choice of cartridges for the pistol in terms of effectiveness downrange.

Once the SIG engineers had cut their teeth on producing the standard pistol, they started improving the basic design, working through World War II until they had created an improved gun of their own by 1944. (Petter had moved back to Switzerland by this time, but it is unclear whether or not he was involved in the SIG work of perfecting the company's spinoffs from his original design.)

Chambered for the 9mm Luger, there were two versions of the new SIG pistol. One became known as the "Neuhausen 44/16", the "44" standing for the year it was perfected and the "16" for the number of rounds in its magazine; the other was dubbed the "Neuhausen 44/8", since it had an 8-round magazine. Neither of the pistols proved to be up to SIG standards, so design work continued. Finally the engineers were satisfied with an 8-round version perfected in 1947; it became the "Selbstladepistole 47/8."

Among the departures the 47/8 made from the Modele 1935A was a modification of the slide rails on the new Swiss design; these rails were lengthened and permitted the slide to ride inside the top of the frame making it very impervious to dirt. Internally the double swinging links that locked the action were discarded and replaced with a camming lug on the barrel. Additionally the awkward slide-mounted safety of the 1935A was replaced with a frame-mounted safety, easily released by a downward stroke of the shooter's thumb.

Although SIG was looking toward military sales of the pistol, the new gun actually appeared first on the commercial market as the "SIG P210", sold with a conversion kit that permitted swapping a barrel to convert the gun from 7.65mm to 9mm Luger. A .22 LR conversion kit was also offered by SIG for the new pistol.

Not all P210s have a "plain Jane" look to them. This P210 has been decorated with engraving and carving by SIG to create a one-of-a-kind "Deluxe" model. [Photo courtesy of Mandall's Shooting Supplies, Inc.]

Meanwhile the Swiss military commenced testing the new pistol, soon adopting the 47/8 a year later as its "M49" (Model 1949). Although expensive, the new gun soon had a loyal following and was adopted by the Danish Army as well as the West German Border Police. To date, over 200,000 M49 pistols have been manufactured and the gun continues to be made in limited quantities for civilian sales.

Like SIG's earlier military guns, the new pistols soon established a reputation for being among the finest in the world with many fans of these guns arguing that they are the very best. However, all was not well at the company headquarters. Swiss export restrictions on firearms prevented SIG from selling its new pistols to many potential buyers. And the Swiss people, even though they enjoyed the freedom of owning firearms almost without restrictions, could only buy so many SIG pistols.

In an effort to get around export laws and red tape, SIG entered several joint production ventures with two German manufacturers, Hammerli and J.P. Sauer & Sohn, to produce variations of its pistols. These guns are somewhat similar to the original SIG pistols but may have modifications in order to meet various perceived market needs as well as to make improvements in the original design.

The SIG engineer's collaboration with those from J.P Sauer & Sohn produced a whole series of new pistols. Based in Eckernforde, Germany, Sauer traces its origins back to the 1800s and has been known over the years for first-rate small arms. Sauer's first military pistols were made in association with Spangenberg, V. Ch. Schilling, and C. G. Haenel to make a well-received revolver, the "Reichsrevolver", marketed in the 1880s. This combined operation only lasted for five years after which the partnership was dissolved and J.P. Sauer & Sohn went back into business on its own, still producing the revolvers it had tooled up to manufacture.

Sauer continued to make a number of pistols over the years including the Bär repeating pistol and the Roth-Sauer designed by Georg Roth. Included in the Sauer lineup was the Model 38H, introduced in 1938; many consider this gun one of the best compact pistols ever created.

Business end of a P220 [Photo courtesy of Sigarms.]

The post-World War II era caused a brief lapse of firearms manufacturing as Sauer reorganized. The firm finally returned to the firearms market in the 1950s with single-action revolvers aimed at the "fast draw" market created in the U. S. by the popularity of TV Westerns. It was at this point that SIG decided to use Sauer's ability to build quality guns; with the contract from SIG to produce a new pistol for export, Sauer finally returned to making quality semiautomatic pistols.

In the early 1970s the Swiss military became interested in upgrading the basic Model 49 design, incorporating new features that were desirable, including a firing pin block for added safety and a double-action trigger pull that would do away with the need for a manual safety. SIG engineers, working with those from Sauer, labored to create a new pistol using the P210 as a starting point. The end result was the P220 which was adopted by the Swiss military as its "M75" pistol in 1975.

Because of Germany's position in the EC (European Community) and because of laws that hamper export of arms from

Switzerland as well as prevent it from becoming a member of the EC, Sauer has become SIG's key to making money worldwide while the expertise of SIG's engineers has been an asset to Sauer as well. Under this partnership, many variations of the SIG-Sauer pistols have sprung up from the original P220 design created for the Swiss military trials. Some of these new models were created to fit into specifications laid down by other potential military buyers. Others, like alloy frames and simplification of the design, have been exploited to reduce both the price tag and overall weight of the firearm.

Among the greatest changes from the original P220, but still a spinoff from its basic design, is the P230, chambered at one time or another for 9x18mm, .380 Auto, .32 ACP, or .22 LR. This gun operates with straight blow-back, lacking any sort of lock up and, as one might expect since the gun is made by Sauer, borrows design features from the Sauer Model 38H. Yet despite the different profile of the pistol (due to the placement of the 38H-style recoil spring around its barrel), most of the inner workings and layout of the P230 can be traced back to the P220.

The SIG-Sauer P220's design was several steps forward from the P210. The most noticeable change is the addition of a decocking lever on the left side of the frame, just ahead of the

P230 [Photo courtesy of Sigarms.]

The light weight and low recoil of the P230 makes it an ideal gun to plink with—or press into service as a defensive weapon. [Photo courtesy of Sigarms.]

upper half of the grip panel. This lever permits lowering the hammer from its cocked position and does away with the need of a safety since the gun can be carried with the hammer down and then fired with a long, "double-action" trigger pull.

Internally the SIG-Sauer designs are simplified from that of the P210 with the newer guns having barrels that lock up in the ejection port rather than with an internal lug. This simplifies manufacture because the barrel locking section can be made from an investment casting rather than a machined part (as is the case with the P210 design).

As an additional safety feature, the P220 and its spinoffs have an internal firing pin safety that prevents the gun firing on the off chance that the hammer drops without being released by the trigger. Only when the trigger is pulled back is the internal safety released, permitting the firing pin free to reach a cartridge. (This feature has since been copied by most modern semiauto pistols produced by other manufacturers.)

The P220 proved to be a popular pistol and soon the Swiss military decided to adopt it as its Model 75, the P210 being gradually retired from service. About the only drawback of the P220 for some shooters was its small magazine capacity—just 9 rounds—and the European-style magazine release located on the base of the grip.

P225 during some torture tests involving dropping in mud followed by a firing of the pistol. [Photo courtesy of Sigarms.]

In an effort to capture more sales, SIG-Sauer engineers created several spinoffs from the P220 design. Among these are the P225 which has an "American" magazine release consisting of a button on the left side of the grip panel and a shortened grip and slide for concealed carry (lowering the magazine capacity by one round); the P226 has an "American" side magazine release and a high-capacity 15-round magazine with a full-size grip and slide. The P228 split the differences between the P225 and P226, giving the new pistol a short grip, shortened slide, 13-round magazine, and side-mounted magazine release.

Since the introduction of these variants, others have sprung up, with a bewildering variety of configurations thanks to chamberings (9mm, .45 ACP, .40 Auto, .38 Super, or .357 SIG), availability of night sights, and a choice of stainless steel, nickel, or blued steel finishes with some models. (A closer look at all these variations will be given in the next chapter.)

The P226 appears to have been created with an eye toward the U. S. Army trials designed to find a replacement for the 1911 .45 semiauto pistol. The most noticeable change in the P226 for

Machinist (top, left) assembling P228 pistol and a brace of P228 alloy frames (bottom, right) being processed for assembly. [Photos courtesy of Sigarms.]

the Army trials was the addition of an ambidextrous magazine release system which was required by the U. S. military's specifications for its new pistol.

The U. S. military's search for a new pistol hadn't occurred overnight. As far back as 1949 the Army had toyed with the idea of adopting a 9mm pistol but finally dropped the idea due to the large inventory of 1911-A1 .45 semiautos left over from WWII. By 1976, the Air Force, which had been arming its guards with .38 Special revolvers, decided to start its own tests for the selection of a 9mm pistol. This was followed a year later by the Department of Defense's decision to develop a new .38-caliber handgun cartridge that would be more effective than either the .38 Special or .45 ACP.

Soon other branches of the military were expressing interest in creating a new pistol or cartridge and it was becoming obvious that a stampede toward the development of the "ultimate" pistol and cartridge was about to begin. In addition to creating a lot of waste through duplicated efforts, the endeavors threatened to flood the American military with a confusing array of ammunition and pistols, making resupply efforts during a war a potential nightmare. The Department of Defense stepped in to head such a problem off, creating the Joint Services Small Arms Program (JSSAP) which would oversee the development of small arms including any new pistols that might be adopted by all or most branches of the U. S. military.

In 1980, after several years of deliberation, the JSSAP recommended that a 9mm Luger pistol be adopted in several versions, one gun to be a standard-sized pistol and the other a smaller gun that might be concealed and which would be more easily carried by an officer or bodyguard. With the decision came the announcement of a series of tests to select the new guns. Any company that was interested would be required to submit 40 guns for testing.

Seeing a potentially huge market opening up, gun manufacturers started scrambling to become a part of things. Beretta, Browning FN, Colt, Heckler & Koch, Smith & Wesson, SIG-Sauer, Steyr, and Walther all expressed interest in being included in the trials and had soon submitted pistols for testing. With the exception of Colt (which presented a revamped 1911-A1 pistol chambered for the 9mm cartridge as their candidate), all the guns submitted were of more or less new designs that were fabricated with an eye toward meeting all the requirements the JSSAP had laid out for the new pistol.

The P226 pistols submitted for the tests were actually manufactured by SIG-Sauer. However, because part of the deal required that the winner of the final contract for new pistols would be required to manufacture the guns within U. S. borders, the P226s were entered on behalf of the Maremont Corporation who had acquired the military manufacturing and marketing rights for the pistol in the U. S. should the gun win the trials and go into production. (Consequently these pistols are sometimes referred to as the "Maremont P226" pistols in conjunction with these tests, even though they were actually manufactured by SIG-Sauer.)

The tests demonstrated shortcomings in many of the guns

submitted. But the SIG-Sauer P226 was a different story; the new pistol proved itself to be super reliable, with only Beretta's Model 92 being able to do as well as the Swiss/German pistols. In the end, the military could fault neither pistol so the Beretta won the contract simply because its firearm carried a lower price tag. In 1985, the JSSAP announced that Beretta was the winner of the new defense contract for 315,930 pistols. Because of its outstanding performance, the SIG-Sauer P226 was designated as an alternate pistol for some government organizations wishing to adopt the pistol; consequently, while the Beretta Model 92 is normally seen in the hands of Army officers, U. S. elite troops and many government agents carry the SIG-Sauer P226, preferring it over the Beretta pistol.

Not a little controversy surrounded the JSSAP tests with many of the companies submitting pistols claiming that the procedures hadn't been fair. Smith & Wesson went so far as to threaten a lawsuit because company officials felt their guns

SIG-Sauer P226 [Photo courtesy of Sigarms.]

The Beretta 951 (top, right) was a forerunner of the 92F (bottom, left) used in US JSSAP tests.

hadn't got a fair shake in the trials. Soon several congressmen wanting to protect gun manufacturers in their districts were jumping into the fray. With legal and political pressures mounting, the JSSAP grudgingly announced a new round of trials before the last installment of 142,282 pistols was purchased for the U. S. military.

This 1988 test was run at the Aberdeen Proving Grounds with Beretta, Smith & Wesson, and Sturm, Ruger & Company all submitting pistols. Again the Beretta won out over its competitors.

This last round of tests was conclusive. Beretta remains the issue pistol for most U. S. military users with some elite troops and some government agencies using some variant of the SIG-Sauer P226 or, in the case of a few hold outs, retaining the old 1911-A1 pistols for use as sidearms.

At the time of this writing another round of tests is going on in the U. S. military, this time to create a special purpose pistol that can be equipped with a silencer as well as a laser aiming device or flashlight. Unfortunately such a pistol dictates a

The Ruger P-85 pistol was a contender in the 1988 JSSAP tests. But the pistol was of a new design and not yet totally debugged; consequently the SIG-Sauer and Beretta entries outshone it.

heavier bullet—getting away from the JSSAP's efforts to keep ammunition consistent within the various branches of the military to simplify resupply of troops. Ever optimistic of Browning's old but reliable design, Colt has submitted a revamped 1911-A1 pistol having an extended grip for the added magazine capacity required in the specifications for the tests; Heckler & Koch created a brand new pistol for the project. Whether either of these guns will fulfill the needs of the government remains to be seen, especially with the current round of cuts in funds for military projects.

SIG-Sauer, for all practical purposes, already offers a pistol that fits the needs for such a special purpose pistol. The pistol is the SIG-Sauer P220 is chambered in .45 ACP. Creation of a threaded barrel and silencer for the P220 and a laser sight/ flashlight attachment would permit this pistol to contend with the Colt and H&K guns. And as will be noted later in this book, there are already "off the shelf" laser and flashlight attachments for this pistol. Could the P220 end up as the choice for this purpose? There's no indication that the P220 is even being involved in the tests, very possibly because of SIG-Sauer's experience with the JSSAP's earlier round of tests. But it isn't beyond the realm of possibility that the P220 might be pressed into service given the fact that the SIG-Sauer guns are already in use and well liked by several special units within the U. S. military. Stranger things have happened.

The SIG-Hammerli target pistol was created shortly after the introduction of the SIG-Sauer P230. The SIG-Hammerli design built on some of the features created for the SIG-Sauer P220.

Hammerli SA, based in Lenzburg, Switzerland, has been famous over the years as the manufacturer of specialized target pistols of the highest quality and accuracy. Many of the company's guns defy classification due to the fact that they are built to target shooter's specifications and used in single-shot "free" pistol competitions where a wide variety of configurations are legal.

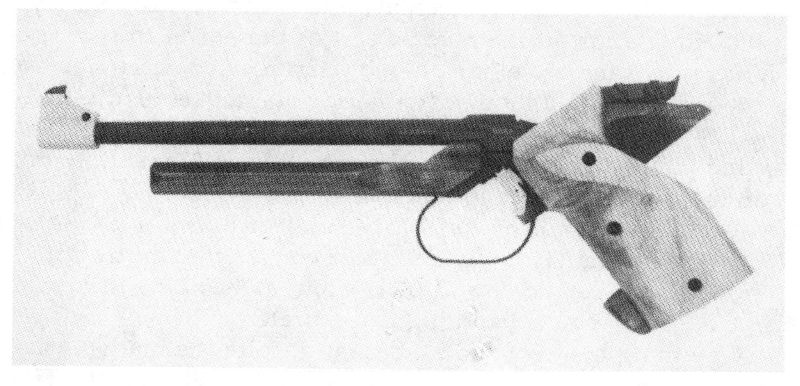

Hammerli free pistols, like this Model 150, almost defy categorization and are far removed from the P240. [Photo courtesy of Sigarms.]

The pistol design produced by the combined SIG and Hammerli engineering teams is a bit different from these fanciful pistols. It was aimed at military contestants who desired target pistols similar to the standard military sidearm and which would fire in a semiauto, rather than a single-shot, mode. Since Switzerland had adopted the SIG 210 as its military pistol, this dictated that the competition gun be as similar to the military arm as possible while still offering a lot of accuracy and reliability with the less powerful target loads fired in competition.

The end result of the collaboration between the two companies was the SIG-Hammerli P240. The P240 resembles the SIG210, though it departs from the original gun in a number of areas with the contoured, hand-hugging pistol grips being the most noticeable external change.

Originally there were two chamberings for the P240, one being for the .38 Special Wadcutter and the other a .22LR pistol, both cartridges being popular with target shooters due to their great potential accuracy. Since the P240's introduction, a .32 S&W Long chambering has been added since this cartridge has become popular with target shooters.

The .32 S&W Long and .38 Special chamberings of the P240 fire from a locked breech which copies the P220 system, locking the top of the barrel in the ejection port. The pistol also employs a belled exterior on the muzzle end of the barrel to secure a tighter fit to the slide and thereby assure more accuracy—a system later copied by many American target semiautos. On the P240 the fit between the barrel and slide is so precise that exchanging parts between two guns will usually result in one gun that fits too tightly to function.

The .22LR version of the P240 uses a fixed barrel and a blowback system, similar to that of the .22 conversion units created for the P210. Like the .38 and .32 versions of the P240, this pistol is carefully assembled and highly accurate.

One thing has remained constant despite the many variations that have sprung up from the original SIG P210: The overall quality of the SIG, SIG-Hammerli, and SIG-Sauer guns always remains high. The P210 and all its variants have a reputation for reliability and workmanship unequaled by another manufacturer.

The price tag on these guns has always been high and is destined to remain so; but purchasers don't mind all that much because they know that the high price is reflected in the outstanding product they're buying. For that reason, the SIG, SIG-Hammerli, and SIG-Sauer pistols are going to be around with a loyal following for a long, long time.

When all the possible combinations of parts and finishes are taken into consideration, there's a huge variety of SIG and SIG-Sauer pistols to be seen in the world market. The majority of pistols will fall into the major categories outlined in this chapter with minor variations being seen in finish (blued, sand/matte, nickel, or K-Kote) as well as the use of stainless steel slides on some models and alloy frames rather than the more traditional blued steel—with the P230 even being seen with a stainless steel frame on the "SL" models. Some guns will also sport "Siglite" for yet other variations of the guns. Throw in customized guns, replacement grips and sights, and various accessories and there's almost no limit to the variations.

Of course finishes are the most striking differences between guns of the same model type. The "blued steel" finish on SIG-Sauer pistols is achieved with black oxide or zinc phosphate with alloy frames anodized to a matching black. Considering the variety of finishes on the various parts of one pistol, it's amazing that the color match-up is generally very good on the "blued" pistols, with only the closest of inspections showing the slight differences in hue between differently finished parts.

The K-Kote finish found on many of the SIG-Sauer guns consists of a dark polymer placed over the final finish for added resistance to moisture. A pistol with the K-Kote coating can withstand 1,000 hours in salt spray without any corrosion, something no standard blued finish can come close to. It should be noted that this coating is external only; internal parts have only the standard blued finish and must be carefully cleaned and oiled just as with any other firearm. Although the majority of K-Kote finishes are black, the color of the polymer is sometimes modified at the SIG-Sauer factory for large orders of pistols. Consequently some military guns will be seen with green K-Kote exteriors or the more rare day-desert tan or camouflage finishes.

Electroless nickel finishes are also available with many of the SIG-Sauer models. While many military and police purchasers avoid this finish because of its slightly reflective qualities, civilian shooters for the most part love the low-maintenance finish and admire the way it looks. Too, nickel tends to be somewhat slick (though not as slick as chrome), aiding somewhat in reliability of the pistol—though reliability has never been a problem with any of the guns covered in this chapter.

Currently almost all of the SIG-Sauer pistols imported into the U. S. are offered with a nickel finished slide version; the exception to this is the P230 which is offered in a stainless steel variant. All other models are offered with a choice of nickel slide, K-Kote, or blued finishes.

Because of various political and training considerations, a few police departments have opted to arm their forces with double-action-only guns that require a heavy trigger pull for each shot, rather than switching to a single-action pull after the first shot. The thinking behind the requirement for such a pistol is that it reduces the chance of accidents without requiring more time spent on the firing range. Sound or not, this has led to the marketing of double-action-only pistols by a number of companies, including SIG-Sauer, in order to fill this demand.

As might be expected, guns marketed around the world have to accommodate a variety of other requirements set down by purchasers. In order to meet some of these, two distinct magazine releases are seen on various SIG-Sauer pistols. One is the "European" style with the release located at the rear edge of the magazine well. The other is the "American" style which places a release button at the side of the grip, just behind the trigger guard. This has led to a pair of submodel designations in early SIG-Sauer catalogs with an "SB" designating an American-style magazine release; newer catalog listings now use an "AM" to designate an American-style release.

The biggest demand these days is for the American-style release. Consequently the current trend with the SIG-Sauer guns appears to be toward making this type of release the standard; it seems likely that eventually the European-style release will vanish from the SIG-Sauer catalog. Already several models are normally seen only with the American-style release.

In addition to the type of magazine release a gun has, the SIG-Sauer product numbers are coded to tell at a glance what a gun's model number, finish, sights, and trigger pull style will be as well. The first numbers are the model number of the gun. These are usually followed by a hyphen and a number showing the chambering of the pistol with "45" indicating a .45 ACP gun; "40", .40 S&W; "38", .38 Super; "9", 9mm Luger; "357", .357 SIG; and "380", .380 ACP.

When all of the "cues" given by catalog numbers are deciphered, a shooter can tell a lot about what the gun will be like just from its model designation. The first letter in the suffix indicates the finish on the gun with "B" (or lack of a letter) designating a blued finish; "T", nickel finish; "K", K-Kote; and "S" stainless steel.

The next letter in the suffix shows whether or not the gun has night sights with an "SS" indicating that it does. An "AM" at or toward the end of the suffix indicates an American-style magazine release (though this is increasingly rare as recently made pistols tend to have this type of release due to its growing popularity); "DAO" (also usually toward the end of the product number) indicates a double-action-only trigger system.

This system is easy to "read." A SIG-Sauer pistol with a product number of "220-45-BSS", for example, would be a P220 model in .45 ACP with a blued finish and night sights while a "228-9-T-DAO" would be a P228 in 9mm with a nickel finish and double-action-only trigger group.

Since grip panels can be exchanged between some models and purchased separately apart from the original pistol, some pistols will be seen with the walnut "accessory" grips sold by SIG and SIG-Sauer. Many of these grips come in a "European" or "American" style to accommodate the two styles of magazine releases. The standard grip panels on the SIG-Sauer guns are black plastic with checker molded into standard-sized guns while the "hide out" compact models often have stippled grips. In addition to the factory plastic and accessory wooden grips, several aftermarket rubberized and wooden grips are also available for these guns (more about these in Chapter 4).

All the SIG-Sauer grips are well designed and when held give the illusion that the pistols are thinner than they really are, especially in the case of the double-column magazine models. Many pistols having a double-column magazine leave the shooter feeling as if he's holding a bat; the good design of the SIG-Sauer high-capacity guns feel thinner than they actually are, giving the shooter a good sense of control. The grip panels and grip angle also make these guns point well for most shooters used to the 1911 auto, Browning "High Power" P35, or other guns with similar grip angles.

The standard recoil spring now found on all the post-1986 SIG-Sauer pistols is the multi-strand twisted wire often seen in European guns and rarely seen in U. S. manufactured weapons. Arguably the merits of the twisted wire spring may be small; but such a system does offer greater resistance to loss of strength over extended use and is especially durable in cold climates. As such, the multi-strand spring is another example of the extra quality that goes into these firearms.

Always catering to a wide variety of potential buyers, SIG-Sauer has also created a well-illustrated owner's manual that gives its instructions in French, English, German, and Spanish. This is backed up by the usual warranties coupled with the usually good service SIG-Sauer requires of its dealers.

Adding to the variety of pistols are those doing custom work on SIG and SIG-Sauer pistols. The expensive price tags of these pistols makes custom work a bit prohibitive. However, it's likely that more than a few of these pistols have been altered in one way or another with pleasing and less-than-pleasing results by little-known gunsmiths interested in creating a customized gun to suit their tastes or those of a client. Engraving, refinishing, and other modifications are all practical with the guns in this chapter. Some of the best custom work being done on the SIG and SIG-Sauer pistols is coming from TJ's Custom Gunworks (see appendix for address).

There has also been some work by competition shooters to rechamber 9mm versions of the SIG-Sauer pistols to fire more potent cartridges like the 9x21mm and 9x22mm, rounds created by lengthening 9mm Luger brass slightly to accommodate more powder. These hot rounds place what was once a "minor" contest cartridge into a "major" category, thanks to a slight increase of power afforded by the lengthened case. Such modifications require careful reloading in order to avoid excessive pressures; a few contest shooters have already trashed their firearms using such cartridges. And ballistically, these cartridges are somewhat iffy and most likely offer little improvement off the playing field. But with high-stakes shooting contests and the inherent accuracy of the SIG-Sauer pistols, it's likely that this trend will continue until a new contest tactic appears—or shooters adopt the new .357 SIG cartridge and gun chambered for it to competition shooting.

The few SIG-Sauer guns showing up in shooting contests are often modified in other ways. Currently the most popular modification is the addition of a compensator which redirects gas from the cartridge upward and rearward to reduce the recoil and muzzle flip of the gun, making a faster second shot practical. But given the steeper price of the SIG-Sauer guns as compared to more "traditional" contest guns like the 1911-A1 .45, it seems likely that the SIG-Sauer guns will always be in the minority at shooting contests.

The SIG and SIG-Sauer pistols are famous for their finishes and overall quality of workmanship, qualities that nearly every gun lives up to. This quality translates into good accuracy and reliability as well as joy of ownership. Most SIG pistols fire into a one-inch group at 25 yards; other manufacturer's guns normally fire into a 2-inch group.

In addition to being accurate, the SIG and SIG-Sauer pistols are noted for their ability to handle a variety of ammunition both in terms of power as well as bullet types. This is an important point because, while semiauto firearms are all somewhat ammunition sensitive, the SIG and SIG-Sauer pistols are less so than most. This makes it possible for these pistols to chug along firing a variety of ammunition that will fail to cycle or even feed in many other semiauto handguns. It also does away with the need to take the guns to a gunsmith for throating or other expensive modifications before they are reliable; the savings through avoiding such expensive gunsmithing work often makes the actual "cost" of the SIG and SIG-Sauer guns more competitive when compared to other guns that aren't very reliable out of the box.

Sigarms, the importer of SIG-Sauer guns into the U. S., takes one extra step to assure reliability in the 9mm guns it sells. Each barrel chamber is carefully gauged to assure dependability. Since American 9mm Luger cartridges are often a bit "fatter" than their European counterparts, guns that work well with European ammunition may jam with U. S. fodder. For this reason Sigarms reams out any tight chambers it finds on pistols coming into the U. S. This makes the pistols brought into the U. S. help maintain the SIG-Sauer reputation for reliability.

Of course all of this reputation for craftsmanship has its price. SIG, SIG-Hammerli, and SIG-Sauer pistols cost considerably more than most other mass produced pistols with the SIG-Sauers currently running about $300 more than similar semiautos offered by American manufacturers. But shooters do get what they pay for when they buy one of these Swiss or German made guns.

The Swiss-made SIG P210 variants as well as the SIG-Hammerli Model 240, are imported into the U. S. by Mandall Shooting Supplies while the SIG-Sauer guns are imported into the U. S. by Sigarms, Inc. A very few of the early SIG-Sauer P225 pistols were imported into the U. S. by Browning as the company's "BDA" (Browning Double Action) model; P220 guns were imported by Interarms as the "220" for a short time; and Hawes also imported several of the SIG guns into the U. S. for a time.

SIG pistols are marked as being made in Switzerland. SIG-Sauer guns have "Made In Germany" or "Made in West Germany" and the model number of the pistol engraved on the right side of the slide and "SIG SAUER" (with the two company names offset rather than hyphenated) inscribed on the left side of the slide, usually along with the cartridge designation.

SIG P210

The Swiss military adopted the SP47/8 in 1949 as its military pistol, designating it the P210. The pistol continued in service until 1975. SIG continues to make the popular pistol for commercial sales and the pistols are known for their accuracy and quality of workmanship. Except for the magazine release which is located on the bottom of the pistol grip and its limited magazine capacity (by modern standards), the pistol is very well designed.

A lanyard loop is to be found on the lower left side of the frame. While generally out of the way for right-handed shooters, this is less than ideal for left-handed users. However, removal of the loop should be approached with caution since it will alter the collector's value of the pistol and dictates a replacement panel for the left side of the pistol to cover the space created by the missing lanyard loop. Best bet is to learn to live with this nearly useless device.

Conveniently located—for right handers—above the left grip panel, the thumb safety is easily swept down by most shooters. However, shooters with smaller hands may find it isn't as easily pushed into the "fire" position as one might hope for. The quick-and-dirty solution to this problem is to remove a bit of the left grip panel below the safety which then gives easy access to the lever.

On new guns the safety lever may be a bit too stiff for easy operation. Generally this problem cures itself and more than a few owners have sat in front of TV sets slipping the safety of their P210s on and off until the lever is worn in and easily manipulated. For those without patience, a faster alternative is to take the pistol to a gunsmith and have him lightly polish the engagement area to make the safety easier to use.

SIG P210-1 [Photo courtesy of Mandall's Shooting Supplies, Inc.]

The P210 has a magazine safety that prevents the gun from firing if the magazine is removed. The big plus of this is that it prevents accidental discharges often associated with amateur gun cleaning. Such accidents occur when a novice removes a magazine without cycling the cartridge out of the chamber, thinking he has emptied the weapon, when in fact a round remains in the chamber. He then squeezes the trigger to drop the hammer, firing the gun. If he's taken the time to keep the gun pointed in a safe direction, not too much harm is done. But most novices who fail to know what is needed to unload a semiauto also don't have the good sense to keep a gun pointed in a safe direction. Consequently such accidental shootings with "empty" pistols often have tragic results. The magazine helps avoid such a disaster.

The magazine safety also makes it possible to store the magazine in one place and the gun with a chambered round in another. Simply jabbing the magazine into place and flipping off the manual safety makes the gun ready to fire—a plus for those wanting a gun to defend against intruders but who also have small children in the home.

On the minus side of the equation, the magazine safety means a person can't reload knowing that he can fire the pistol if he needs to. While such situations are rare in combat, it isn't impossible to imagine a circumstance where it might occur, especially given the limited magazine capacity of the P210. Like everything else, the magazine safety has definite pluses and minuses which owners should be aware of and which they should work around.

There are five distinct submodels of the P210, each designated by a suffix number. They are mechanically identical with the differences mostly being in fit, finish, sights, and barrel length.

The P210-1 has a highly polished finish and wooden grips; the P210-2 has a matte finish with checkered black plastic grips. There is no "-3" version of the P210; apparently this gun was produced in-house but never had any military or police buyers for it. The P210-4 is produced for the West German Border Police; the P210-5 is a target version of the pistol and has a 5.8-inch barrel with the front sight mounted on it to create a longer field of view. The P210-6 is another target version of the pistol with a standard-length barrel. Both of the target guns have micro-adjustable rear sights that can compensate for both windage and elevation; the other guns have a rear sight that is drift adjustable for windage. In addition to these distinct models, SIG engravers will also create a "Deluxe" model for buyers, starting with one of the basic guns and carefully engraving it according to the buyer's wishes. Needless to say, such firearms cost a pretty penny, but most owners feel they're worth every cent.

The P210-1, -2, and -6 are seen in 7.65mm or 9mm versions and these three submodels can be converted to one or the other cartridge by changing barrels and recoil springs. A .22 LR conversion unit is also available which can be used on any model by exchanging the barrel, recoil spring, slide, and magazine. The .22 conversion kit was originally designed for military training but is popular with civilian and police users wanting to practice in areas where the noise or penetration of centerfire cartridges is prohibitive. Undoubtedly a few hunters also make use of the .22 LR conversion for taking small game. Because some European and South American countries restrict gun ownership to arms that aren't chambered for military rounds (apparently in an effort to keep citizens from overthrowing the government), the 7.65mm version of the P210s are popular in many of these areas, including Italy.

During the 1970s, there was talk of a P210 chambered for .45 ACP, perhaps in an effort to cut into the American market. However this submodel was never built, most likely because several of the SIG-Sauer models were chambered in this cartridge and, because of greater ease in exporting the German-made guns, hit most of the potential sales that might have been made by a .45-caliber P210.

The P210 has a big following around the world. In his book, *The 100 Greatest Combat Pistols*, Timothy J. Mullin has this to say about the pistol. "Without a doubt, this has got to be the best 9mm pistol in the world."

It's hard to beat an endorsement like that.

P210 specifications: Over-all length: 8.46 inches; Weight (unloaded): 1.98 lbs.; Barrel length: 4.72 inches; Magazine capacity: 8.

P210-2, shown with 22 LR conversion slide/barrel assembly. [Photo courtesy of Mandall's Shooting Supplies, Inc.]

P210-5 target pistol. [Photo courtesy of Mandall's Shooting Supplies, Inc.]

P210-6 target pistol. [Photo courtesy of Mandall's Shooting Supplies, Inc.]

SIG-SAUER P220

The SIG-Sauer P220 was designed around the SIG P210 as a joint effort of SIG and J.P. Sauer & Hohn of West Germany and has the distinction of being the first modern semiauto pistol to do away with a manual safety. Presently all P220s are manufactured at the Sauer factory in Eckernforde, Germany.

The P220 has a double-action trigger and a firing pin block which allows the pistol to be safely carried without the need of a thumb safety or similar device. The decocking lever at the upper front of the left grip panel safely lowers the hammer without the need for the shooter to use his thumb to keep the hammer from dropping against the firing pin; the internal firing pin safety and a half-cock position on the hammer keeps the hammer lowering safe. On most P220s, when the decocking lever is pulled down, the hammer falls to half cock position; this isn't true of most of the other later pistols in the SIG-Sauer lineup which drop the hammer all the way forward with the firing pin being secured by the internal safety.

This arrangement makes the P220 convenient to use and does away with the need for a manual safety. To load the gun, one simply needs to insert a magazine, rack the slide back, and then release the slide. These actions chamber a cartridge and leave the hammer back. The gun can now be fired in a single-action, short-stroke trigger pull (of about 4 to 5 pounds). Or, if the gun isn't to be fired immediately, the hammer-drop lever can be used to safely lower the hammer. This latter procedure permits firing the gun with a longer, double-action trigger pull that requires around 14-15 pounds of pressure. With no manual safety to fool with, all the shooter needs to do is draw and fire the pistol when it is carried loaded with the hammer down.

Following the first shot with the double-action pull, the gun reverts to a lighter, single-action with the hammer back and the trigger requiring only 4 to 5 pounds of pressure to drop it (the only exception to this is with the double-action-only models which have a long, heavy trigger pull that is consistent from shot to shot). When a follow-up shot isn't required, then the hammer drop lever can again make the firearm safe to carry in a holster.

SIG-Sauer P220. [Photo courtesy of Sigarms.]

P220 with "blued" finish. [Photo courtesy of Sigarms.]

Of course some shooters dislike the heavier pull of a double-action shot. But most users of the P220 (and its sister guns) are willing to put up with this because of the added convenience the system offers. (Diehards can employ a single-action pull on their first shot by thumbing the hammer back as they draw the gun. Provided the trigger finger is kept out of the trigger guard, this is a relatively safe practice and nearly as fast as the manipulation of a manual safety on most other firearms equipped with one. This method of operation is not the most ideal, however, and is best avoided by most shooters.)

Like other SIG-Sauer pistols, the P220 has an internal firing pin safety that locks the firing pin in place until the trigger is pulled back. Once the safety is released by the trigger, the hammer can impart enough force to the firing pin to propel it forward and ignite the primer of the cartridge. If the trigger isn't being pulled so the safety locks the firing pin in place, then it can't reach the cartridge.

Once the cartridge fires, the rearward movement of the slide disengages the trigger so the firing pin again locks up. Only when the trigger is released and then pulled back again will the firing pin safety release the firing pin. This system makes accidental firings nearly impossible, provided the shooter doesn't place his finger on the trigger until he's ready to fire the gun.

To simplify manufacture, the P220 and other SIG-Sauer pistols use a barrel that locks into the ejection port. For this reason, no modifications to either of the mating surfaces should be made with these guns. During the instant a cartridge is fired, the barrel and slide are locked together momentarily as they recoil rearward about 0.12 inch. At this point the rear of the barrel tilts downward, unlocking from the ejection port and releasing the slide which continues rearward to cycle the action for the next shot, stripping a round off the magazine and chambering. When the magazine is empty, the slide is caught by the slide catch which locks the slide to the rear, making it obvious that the gun is empty.

In addition to simplifying manufacture, the lock up of the barrel in the ejection port makes the gun more reliable since the design dictates a larger ejection port. This translates into a bigger "hole" for empties to jump through, thereby minimizing the chances that they'll fail to eject. Such "stovepipe jams" sometimes occur in guns with small ejection ports; such jams are very, very rare with the SIG-Sauer pistols.

Perhaps with a nod toward military buyers, the P220, like most of the other SIG-Sauer versions of the gun, lacks a magazine safety. This makes it possible to fire the gun without the magazine in place, a point to be remembered when getting ready to clean the firearm. Shooters must always *first* remove the magazine and *then* cycle the slide to be sure the P220 is empty.

The magazine release on the P220 on guns made before the mid-1980s are all located on the base of the grip. This changed in 1986 when SIG-Sauer revamped the basic design of the P220, building on the improvements created with subsequent models the company had introduced since the creation of the P220.

The most noticeable change in the post-1986 P220s was the offering of two styles of magazine release, one being the traditional European catch located at the base of the grip, and the other being the "American-style" magazine release on the side of the frame where it can be reached by the thumb of a right-handed shooter (or the forefinger with lefties). The new series of guns also saw the introduction of the P220 chambered for the .45 ACP, apparently in an effort to hit more of the U. S. market.

Another change initiated at this point included the reworking of the P220's grips, modifying them to duplicate the "hand pleasing" style of the P226. Other modifications include the deletion of the lanyard loop from the grip, the replacement of the single-strand recoil spring by a multi-strand style, and slight alterations to the ejector and extractor to reduce the velocity of ejected brass (thereby minimizing the chance of injury to bystanders).

Very early post-1986 guns having American-style magazine releases sometimes had magazine release button lugs that would permit magazines to occasionally drop out of place during firing. This was cured with a redesigned catch having deeper lugs and a beefed up magazine catch spring. (These are available as a retrofit part for the few guns introduced with these faulty catches.)

A disassembly lever is located on the left side of the frame slightly over and to the front of the trigger. The slide lock/release is located at the top of the left grip plate. This release is a bit awkward to reach for some right handers, though most shooters familiar with the pistol have little problem with it; for left-handed shooters, it's easier to simply retract the slide with the off hand once a loaded magazine has been inserted into the gun rather than fool with the release; some lefties have also discovered they can move their thumb over to the left side of the pistol to activate the release (or the hammer drop), but this takes some practice to carry this out quickly without danger of dropping the firearm.

The P220 is available in 9mm Luger, 7.65 Luger, .38 Super, and .45 ACP. Like the P210, this pistol has a .22 LR adapter for use in training. An alloy frame helps keep the overall weight of the pistol down; a modular steel insert actually takes the brunt of recoil on the frame, making it as durable as an all-steel frame. This coupling of steel to alloy frame gives the pistol a much greater "life expectancy" than those of other manufacturers which employ only an alloy frame on their guns without any steel interface in key stress areas.

Many shooters feel that the P220 chambered for the .45 ACP is the best gun available for this cartridge. Part of the reason for this is the reputation for dependability it shares with other SIG-Sauer pistols. And some of the reason is in the convenient controls and comfortable grip that makes this gun a good pointer and delightful to shoot. But much of this satisfaction with the P220 in its .45 chambering is due to the reduced felt recoil which results from the gun's heavy slide coupled with a stiff recoil spring. This translates into a spreading out of the recoil impulse that's considerably more comfortable than the jolt that results with many other pistols chambered for the .45 round.

The standard P220 in 9mm was adopted by the Swiss Army as its Pistol 75; the Japanese Self-Defence Force as well as several Special Forces units of other countries have also adopted this pistol. All versions appear to have hooked trigger guards, though the more rounded guard of the P228 suggests this may change in the near future.

Specifications for .45 ACP P220: Over-all length: 7.79 inches; overall height 5.63 inches; Weight (unloaded with magazine): 1.76 lbs.; Barrel length: 4.41 inches; Magazine capacity: 7.
Specifications for .38 Super P220: Over-all length: 7.79 inches; overall height 5.63 inches; Weight (unloaded with magazine): 1.84 lbs.; Barrel length: 4.41 inches; Magazine capacity: 9.
Specifications for 9mm P220: Over-all length: 7.79 inches; overall height 5.63 inches; Weight (unloaded with magazine): 1.84 lbs.; Barrel length: 4.41 inches; Magazine capacity: 9.

SIG-SAUER P225

The P225 is an aluminum-framed, chopped version of the P220 which was created in 1975 in an effort to capture the call for a new pistol by the West German Police. The perceived need was created by the Palestinian terrorist attack during the 1972 Olympics during which most of the hostages taken were killed due to a botched rescue attempt. As West Germany authorities reviewed the many mistakes that the government had made in the failed rescue, it became apparent that the outdated firearms the police were using needed to be replaced.

Among the requirements for the new pistol that would be issued to police anti-terrorist units was that the new handgun wouldn't require removal of a safety before it could be fired and that it be both durable and reliable, able to survive a 10,000-round torture test with a minimum of failures. The new gun was slated to replace all the pistols then being used by the West German police. Because the P226 met almost all of the specifications except for its size, SIG-Sauer engineers went to work to reduce its overall length and height, creating a "new" pistol, the "P225", which was then submitted to the West German government for testing. When the last of the trials were concluded, one gun was a clear winner; the P225 was well ahead of the other contenders.

The Germans started purchasing the new pistols, designating the model as their P6 ("Pistole 6"). In addition to issuing the P6 to anti-terrorist squads, the pistol soon became the standard pistol for a number of German police forces including the Bundesgrenzschutz (Border Police), Bereitschaftpolizei (Police Field Force Reserve), the Federal Customs Police, and the Railroad Police and smaller forces in various German states. (Since then many Swiss police agencies have also adopted the P225 as their issue sidearm.)

Some P225 models including those issued in Germany as the P6, have their magazine release at the bottom of the pistol grip. Most newer guns have the "American" magazine release, a very good feature for small capacity pistols like the P225 since it makes it easy to quickly reload the pistol. Generally these guns have a squared-off, hooked trigger guard which was popular with most 1970s-vintage pistols from a variety of manufacturers.

Issue sights are of three patterns. One is the plain black square-post/square-notch sights; the other is the "Stavenhagen" pattern that places a white square under the rear sight notch and a white ball on the front sight, a combination some find of help in acquiring the target in low light conditions. The Siglite night sights are similar to the latter sight design but have tritium elements embedded in the areas sporting painted dots on the Stavenhagen configuration.

Like other short-barreled 9mm pistols, the reduced sighting radius of the P225 may make for a bit less accuracy in the hands of some shooters when compared to longer-barreled pistols. This shorter barrel may also create a slight increase in muzzle flash, though with quality ammunition this probably won't be noticeable. The P225 is only chambered for the 9mm Luger and generally has black plastic, checkered grip panels.

The "American" version of the P225 has apparently been adopted by some parts of the U. S. Secret Service, most likely because the lower capacity of the magazine translates to a lighter carrying weight when compared to the heavier loaded weights of most double-column guns. An added plus is that the P225 is similar to the P226 which is popular with this branch of government making training simpler and permitting switching from one gun to the other with a minimum of fuss. The P225 is also carried by the Special Forces of several different countries for much the same reason.

Specifications for P225: Over-all length: 7.08 inches; overall height: 5.14 inches; Weight (unloaded with magazine): 1.81 lbs.; Barrel length: 3.86 inches; Magazine capacity: 8.

"American" version of the P225 [Photo courtesy of Sigarms.]

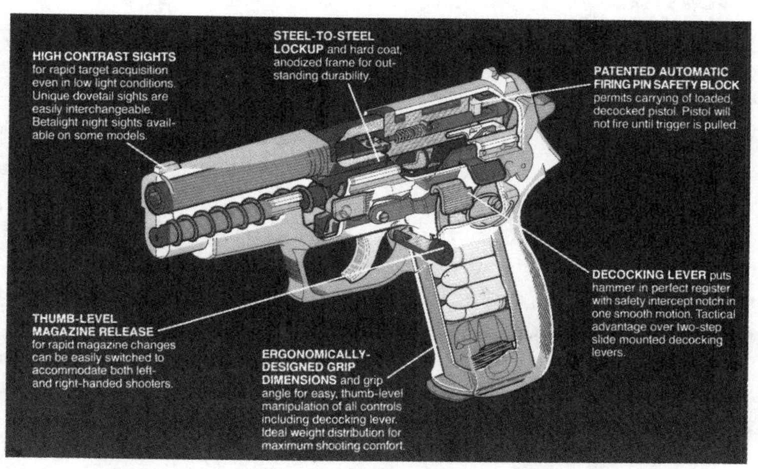

Cutaway of P225. [Drawing courtesy of Sigarms.]

As this ad suggests, the P225 has become a favorite of police users worldwide. [Photo courtesy of Sigarms.]

SIG-SAUER P226

The P226 apparently was created with an eye toward the requirements laid out by the U. S. JSSAP when it was searching for a new pistol for U. S. troops. The P226 is similar to the P225 but has a double row magazine; interestingly, this increase of magazine capacity dictated only slightly more than a tenth of an inch increase in the width of the grip over that of the single-column P225, thanks to some very careful design work by SIG-Sauer engineers. The grip panels are normally black plastic with checkering molded into them.

The P226 passed the JSSAP tests with flying colors. Building on the good publicity gained during the tests, SIG-Sauer introduced a commercial P226 pistol which retained nearly all of the features of the gun submitted for U. S. military tests.

Thanks to JSSAP requirements, the commercial version of the pistol is blessed with a magazine release on the side of the pistol grip. Another of the JSSAP requirements was that the gun have either a reversible magazine release or one that could be operated ambidextrously. SIG-Sauer engineers opted for a reversible design.

Despite the fact that the magazine catch on the commercial P226 can be reversed for left-handed shooters, most lefties will find the gun isn't totally accommodating. The roadblock to full ambidextrous operation is the hammer-lowering lever and slide release levers which—for left handers—are awkward if not impossible to operate with just one hand or without shifting the gun in the hand. Like most other handguns, the P226 is more ideally suited for right-handers; left-handed shooters should plan on spending a lot of extra time practicing with these guns to overcome any handicaps the right-side controls may cause.

P226 [Photo courtesy of Sigarms.

Perhaps building on data gleaned from the JSSAP tests, newer P226 pistols have "grit grooves" cut into the slide rails where the frame and slide mate. This extra space gives dirt particles somewhere to move to as the slide cycles during firing, permitting the gun to clean itself somewhat when operated in dirty environments. Of course if any gun gets dirty enough it will fail to operate reliably and the P226 is no exception to this rule. But engineering this extra into the P226 makes it even more reliable and is a nice touch on the part of SIG-Sauer designers.

The performance of the P226 in the U. S. military trials of the 1980s has proven it is one of the best, if not the best, choices for a combat pistol. Consequently it has been adopted by a number of law enforcement agencies in the U. S. and Canada and elsewhere in the world including the U. S. Navy's SEALS who reportedly refused delivery of JSSAP-selected Beretta pistols and insisted on purchasing the P226 instead.

The P226 has also apparently been adopted by some FBI units (after the failure of the 10mm Auto cartridge to live up to expectations), as well as the U. S. Secret Service government official protection teams, the Drug Enforcement Administration, the Internal Revenue Service, and the National Marine Fisheries Services. England has chosen the P226 to replace its Browning High Power (P35) pistols, apparently with the more compact P228 being used for officers or others needing a more compact pistol; the Royal Canadian Mounted Police also carry a P226 at their sides. And, needless to say with all its popularity among military and police users, the pistol also enjoys a large following among civilian shooters.

The SIG-Sauer P226 is available in both the standard double/single-action configuration as well as newer double-action-only versions. This double-action-only version lacks a single-action notch position on the hammer making it impossible to thumb the hammer back for a more accurate shot. While most police users may never notice the difference, many civilian shooters prefer to have this option and will therefore be happier with the double/single-action arrangement of the original pistol. Except for the difference in trigger actions, these two guns are otherwise nearly identical.

During the mid-1980s, shortly after the introduction of the P226 to the U. S. marketplace, police users in Indiana noted that the P226 double-action pull was a bit long for their female shooters, creating a potential disaster if a fast first shot was needed. SIG-Sauer engineers went to work to solve the problem and created a new trigger which is about one eighth of an inch shorter with a greater curve to it. Although a minor change in size, coupled with the new angle of curve this has proven to be perfect for shooters with smaller hands—as well as those with large mitts. Consequently this trigger design has now become standard for all the P226 guns. (For those owning guns with the old-style trigger, it is possible to have it replaced with the newer style.)

In addition to the standard magazine, SIG-Sauer manufactures an optional 20-round magazine. This will undoubtedly become as rare as hen's teeth in the U. S. thanks to the

Reworked trigger reduces the length of pull on P226 guns, making it a favorite of all types of shooters whether they have small or large hands. [Photo courtesy of Sigarms.]

ill-conceived 1994 ban of the manufacture and importation of magazines having greater than 10-round capacity.

Professional bodyguard, gun consultant, and firearms writer Leroy Thompson is one of the "converts" to the P226 (as well as its sister, the P225). A man who depends on a pistol in potentially life-and-death situations, Thompson has carefully evaluated a variety of pistols over many years and, despite the many new innovations he's seen, until recently carried a Browning High Power as his gun of choice both when he was "on the job" as well as when he needed a "just in case" firearm around his home.

But this changed in 1987 after he evaluated the P225 and P226 for a small foreign government interested in buying new pistols for its military. After putting the two SIG-Sauer pistols through their paces, Thompson was extremely impressed with the guns. So much so that he retired his High Power as well as the H&K P7 and S&W 469 pistols which he often carried as backup to the Browning. Now he carries the P226 as his primary gun and the P225 as his backup.

Writing in the February, 1987 issue of *Combat Handguns*, Thompson had this to say about the P226, "...in simple terms: It shoots very, very straight; it's extremely safe; it's highly reliable; it's easy to maintain. It's what a combat handgun should be—deadly efficient. It looks mean, and it is mean!"

Specifications for P226: Over-all length: 7.71 inches; overall height: 5.47 inches; Weight (unloaded with magazine): 1.87 lbs.; Barrel length: 4.41 inches; Magazine capacity: 15.

SIG-Sauer P226 "Jubilee"

SIG celebrated its 125th anniversary with the introduction of a commemorative P226 which, in the company's catalog, was dubbed the "Jubilee Pistol." Although the Jubilee is basically identical to the standard P226, it has many expensive touches that one might expect on a limited-edition pistol.

The Jubilee has hand-carved European walnut grips with a deep floral pattern carved into its surface. Gold wire inlays fill the lettering, model designation, and other engraving on the slide and frame. The trigger, hammer, decocking lever, slide-catch, and magazine release button are all gold plated.

Each gun came with a custom-made carrying case with a hand-tooled exterior and a white interior with a plaque telling about the gun. The case also had a built-in combination lock. *Specifications for P226 Jubilee: Over-all length: 7.71 inches; overall height: 5.47 inches; Weight (unloaded with magazine): 1.87 lbs.; Barrel length: 4.41 inches; Magazine capacity: 15.*

SIG-Sauer P228

The P228 was introduced late in 1989 and combines a short barrel with a short grip to create a compact pistol. In theory, a pistol like the P228 with a double-column magazine should have a wider profile than a single-column magazine. But when the P228 is compared to the single-column P225, this isn't the case. Thanks to the design abilities of SIG-Sauer engineers, the newer, double-column gun has the same circumference of grip as the single-column magazine gun. This gives users a compact pistol with lots of firepower, something many potential buyers

P226 Jubilee sports gold inlay and plating on its controls and carved grip plates. [Photo courtesy of Sigarms.]

are often looking for. The reduced girth of the P228 (especially when compared to the P226) also makes it an ideal pistol for those with small hands who are looking for a high-capacity handgun.

The shorter height of the grip dictates a shorter, 13-round magazine. However, magazines designed for the P226 fit the P228, making it possible to carry "backup" reloads with 15 or even 20 rounds ready to go after the magazine in the pistol is exhausted. While most defensive situations wouldn't require such massive firepower (most gunfights end with just one or two shots), the ability to lay down such firepower undoubtedly would appeal to bodyguards or others who might be facing a heavily armed foe or terrorists.

It's this reduction in size that has caused the P228 to be adopted by some government agencies in the U. S. as an alternate to larger service pistols including the P226; in fact the P228 has been designated as the "M11 Pistol" by the U. S. Military, adding yet another type of weapon to an arsenal that was supposed to get smaller once a "standard" 9mm pistol was adopted. The British Army has adopted the P226 as its standard pistol with the P228 as its alternate, perhaps a wiser decision given the similarity of the two pistols.

A few U. S. police departments, ever looking for a standard gun that fits both male and female hands, large and small, have also adopted the P228 as their *single* standard pistol. This makes a lot of sense in many ways since the gun is not uncomfortable for those with large hands to use while being ideal for small hands and doesn't lose a lot of firepower with its slightly smaller magazine. The small size also makes the weapon easy to conceal for police detectives, giving police departments a one-gun-fits-all issue weapon.

The P228 is offered with the standard blue/black, nickel slide, and K-Kote finishes with standard or optional Siglite night sights. With an eye toward police sales, a double-action-only model of the P228 is sold as well as the standard double/single-action model. All versions of this gun are chambered for 9mm Luger.

The front of the trigger is grooved—a feature some shooters like and others dislike but can live with. The trigger is nicely rounded making the pull seem lighter than it is by spreading out the pressure on the trigger finger. To aid concealability, the trigger guard is also more arched than on other models of the SIG-Sauer guns and lacks the front hook found on the other models.

With an eye toward comfortable concealed carry, the grip panels on the P228 lack the checkering found on the P226. Instead, the panels have a sandpaper-like stippling that affords

P228 pistol with K-Kote finish and blued finish (inset). [Photo courtesy of Sigarms.]

a good grip but is kinder to skin and clothing when the pistol is carried concealed.

Specifications for P228: Over-all length: 7.08 inches; Overall height: 5.35 inches; Weight (unloaded with magazine): 1.82 lbs.; Barrel length: 3.86 inches; Magazine capacity: 13.

P229

Introduced in 1991, the P229 is nearly identical to the P228, but is offered in a choice of 9mm or .40 S&W chambers. This pistol has the distinction of being assembled in the U. S. from an alloy frame and parts made by SIG-Sauer in Germany with a stainless steel slide manufactured in America at the company's Exeter, New Hampshire plant.

The slide departs from the standard construction of the SIG-Sauer pistols in order to resist the wear and tear given it by the higher pressures of the .40 S&W cartridge. While standard SIG-Sauer slides are two stamped steel shells pinned to a steel breachblock, the P229 is constructed from a single chunk of stainless steel that is forged into shape. The P229 also departs from the standard design a bit with narrower grip grooves that mate it to the slide; the recoil spring in the P229 is stiffer in .40 S&W versions of the P229, a fact dictated by the greater recoil of the cartridge. Like the P228, the P229 has stippled, rather than checkered, plastic grips.

The .357 SIG round which some P229s have recently been chambered for is the brainchild of SIG engineers. Working with Federal Cartridge personnel in 1993, SIG created the bottle-necked cartridge which will fit into the P229 .40 S&W magazine making it possible to use magazines already in production to produce this gun. (The slide, frame, and other parts of the gun are also virtually identical to that of the .40-caliber P229.)

Ballistically, the 125-grain .357 SIG bullet leaves the muzzle of the P229 at nearly the same velocity as the .357 Magnum bullet travels. Since the .357 Magnum has proven itself to be *the* most reliable handgun cartridge in terms of its ability to stop fights with just one "hit" on a human target, this gives the .357 SIG a lot of potential as a defensive round.

Firing such a powerful cartridge from a semiauto pistol isn't

P229 chambered for .357 SIG [Photo courtesy of Sigarms.]

an unpleasant experience. Unlike a revolver which does little to soak up recoil, a semiauto makes firing such a powerful cartridge a more pleasant proposition by absorbing the recoil as the slide travels rearward. Physicists will maintain that all the recoil energy is there with both types of actions; but when the energy is spread out with a semiauto action instead of coming in one massive jolt, it makes all the difference in the world. This makes the P229 a better bet than a revolver for anyone but a masochist.

Whether or not the great ballistic potential of this cartridge and gun will catch on with the shooting public remains to be seen. A lot of newly introduced cartridges have bit the dust when shooters all but ignored them, instead embracing older familiar cartridges. But a few like the .40 S&W have made the grade so it's possible that citizens, police officers, or even competition shooters, interested in the power offered by the .357 SIG coupled with the compact size of the P229, might decide to carry one of these guns. Only time will tell.

On 9mm, .40, and .357 versions of the P229, the stainless steel slide is "blued" to match the frame; "SL" models with a slide keeping its stainless-steel finish are not currently offered in the Sigarms catalog. The P229 models accept optional Siglite night sights and are available in double-action-only and double/single-action models.

Specifications for the P229 9mm: Over-all length: 7.08 inches; Overall height: 5.35 inches; Weight (unloaded): 1.91 lbs.; Barrel length: 3.86 inches; Magazine capacity: 13.

Specifications for the P229 .40: Over-all length: 7.08 inches; Overall height: 5.35 inches; Weight (unloaded): 1.91 lbs.; Barrel length: 3.86 inches; Magazine capacity: 12.

Specifications for the P229 .357 SIG: Over-all length: 7.08 inches; Overall height: 5.35 inches; Weight (unloaded): 1.91 lbs.; Barrel length: 3.86 inches; Magazine capacity: 12.

SIG-Sauer P230 and P230SL

The SIG-Sauer P230 design couples many of the P220's features with the barrel/recoil system of the Sauer Model 38H. As such, the P230 has a fixed barrel, pinned to the frame, and operates with straight blowback rather than using a delayed locking system as on other SIG-Sauer pistols. The pistol's hammer is nearly concealed by the rear of the frame with only the spur protruding for use in cocking for a single-action shot.

The P230 uses a decocking lever, internal firing pin safety, and double-action trigger for a fast first shot, all being similar to those on other SIG-Sauer guns. The hammer drop lowers the hammer to an "intercept notch" that is similar to the half cock on some other pistols. The gun is then fired from this point during the double-action trigger pull of the initial shot. The only time the hammer would actually be pulled back from its full down position would be if it dropped on a cartridge that failed to fire or the pistol was being dry fired. The intercept notch coupled with the automatic firing pin safety makes this gun very safe to carry loaded.

The P230 has the European style magazine release, located at the rear base of the magazine well. However, this isn't as much of a problem with a "pocket" pistol as with a full size gun. In fact, it can be an asset since the American-style side button release can sometimes be inadvertently activated, especially in concealed carry; while the same event can also happen with the European style release, it is generally less common. Furthermore, since a gun like the P230 is apt to be employed for self-defense at very close ranges, the need for a "speed reload" is problematical at best. All in all, the use of the European release on this gun makes good sense when it's most likely intended purpose is taken into consideration.

The pistol was introduced in 1977, chambered for the then-new "9mm Police" which Sauer apparently created just for this pistol. The 9mm Police is slightly larger than the 9mm Short (.380 ACP) and falls into the range of the 9mm Makarov and pre-WWII "Ultra" cartridge. Despite the slight advantages all of these cartridges seem to have on paper, in real life they offer little more than the .380 ACP—and are more expensive to produce in many cases due to limited demand for the rounds. Consequently the P230 is now normally seen chambered for the .380 ACP which is readily available worldwide with a variety of bullet configurations suitable for plinking, hunting, or self-defense without excessive damage to the pocketbook.

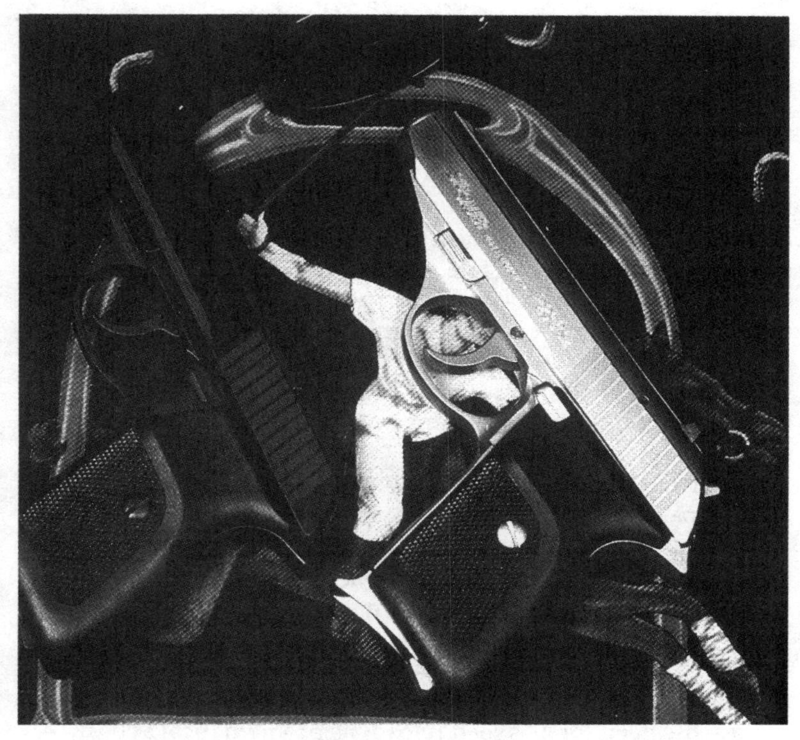

Blued-finish P230 (left) and stainless steel version (right). [Photo courtesy of Sigarms.]

As this ad suggests, the P230 is a popular woman's pistol as well as a first choice of men looking for a quality hideout pistol. [Photo courtesy of Sigarms.]

The standard P230 has a light alloy frame anodized black to match its carbon steel parts; this light frame helps keep the overall weight of the pistol low. The P230SL is the stainless steel version of the gun with both the frame and slide constructed of stainless steel. Currently the P230 is offered in the U. S. only in the .380 ACP chambering.

On most P230SLs, the sights are also stainless steel. This makes them impervious to most environmental dangers, but the sight picture presented by stainless sights is less than ideal in some lighting conditions. While a shooter can go to a lot of work in replacing the rear sight with a blued-steel one, the front sight is an integral part of the slide; the quick but satisfactory fix is to simply dab a bit of paint on front and rear sights, touching them up from time to time as the paint wears off.

Policeman and firearms expert Lt. Gary Paul Johnston wrote about the P230 pistol in the August, 1988 issue of *Combat Handguns.* After carrying a P230 around for several weeks while on vacation and giving it a thorough testing, he had this to say about the pistol: "In addition to being compact, the P230 is one of the most comfortable guns I have ever held, mainly due to its perfectly contoured stocks which make it feel like an extension of one's hand. Yet, the pistol is slim, and in traveling through seventeen states, I found it comfortable and concealable in just the pocket of my Levis, even though it's about a half inch longer than the Walther PPK/S."

In short, the P230 comes about as close to perfection as one can expect. It's a super-reliable compact pistol ideal for a variety of purposes.

Specifications for the P230: Overall length: 6.61 inches; Overall height: 4.68 inches; Weight (unloaded with magazine): 1.08 lbs.; Barrel length: 3.62 inches; Magazine capacity: 7.

Specifications for the P230 SL: Overall length: 6.61 inches; Overall height: 4.68 inches; Weight (unloaded with magazine): 1.4 lbs.; Barrel length: 3.62 inches; Magazine capacity: 7.

SIG-Hammerli P240

The P240 combines elements of the P210 and P220 with its own unique features dictated by its use as a target gun. As might be expected with a pistol designed for contest work, the P240 has a rear target sight that is fully adjustable for windage and elevation with micrometer screw knobs. Grips on these guns are generally of the wrap-around, target style with a pronounced thumb rest, all of which dictate either right-hand or left-hand holds according to the grip configuration. The trigger on the P240 is also adjustable.

The slide release, safety, and magazine release of the P240 are virtually identical to those of the P210. The trigger guard on the P240 is longer, a plus for those wearing gloves during cold-weather shooting.

The .38 Special and .32 S&W Long chamberings of the P240 operate with a lockup similar to that of the SIG-Sauer pistols and can accommodate wadcutter bullets—not an easy design task since these are rimmed cartridges created for revolvers. The .22 LR model operates with a blow-back system, pulling off much the same trick as its center-fire counterparts by reliably feeding rimmed cartridges that aren't ideally suited for semiauto actions. But the SIG-Hammerli engineers did a good job; most of the P240 pistols will digest target loads without problem as long as the gun is kept clean. (In addition to using the gun for contest work, many shooters who will fire the .32 or .38 version

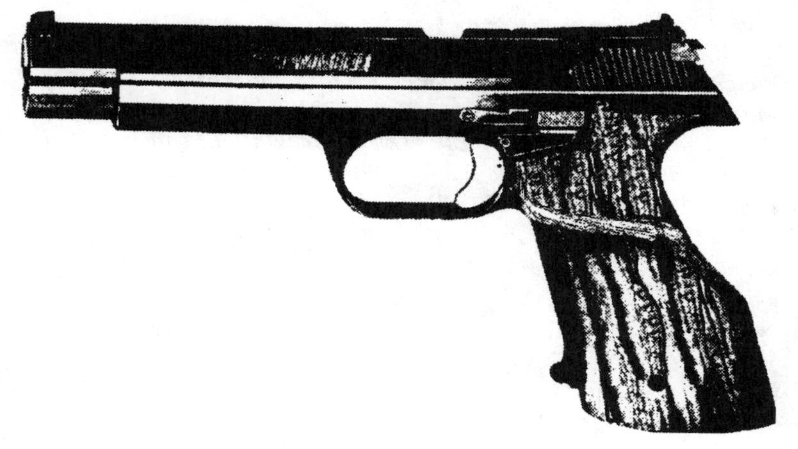

of the P240 during contests employ the .22 version of the pistol both to reduce the cost of ammunition as well as to permit practice in areas where the lower noise and penetration of the .22 LR are important pluses.)

Cleaning these guns is important, due to their tight tolerances as well as the potential problems in feeding a rimmed cartridge through a semiauto action. Since many of the parts in the P240 are hand-fitted, great care must be taken in replacing parts and barrels or other assemblies. Parts from one pistol should not be exchanged with another.

Best accuracy is obtained with target-grade cartridges in the case of the two centerfire cartridges; many shooters find hand-loaded ammunition tailored to their personal pistol offers the best results. With the .22 LR, low-power target ammunition is the first choice for accuracy; again, experimenting to discover what manufacturer's ammunition works best in any given gun will trim down the size of groups being fired and maintain a reliable cycling of the action.

Currently only the .32 S&W Long chambering of the P240 is being imported in the U. S. by Mandall's Shooting Supplies, Inc. Like other versions of this pistol, these have a blued finish.

Specifications for P240 .38 Special: Overall length: 9.74 inches; Weight (unloaded with magazine): 2.2 lbs.; Barrel length: 6 inches; Magazine capacity: 5.

Specifications for P240 .32 S&W Long: Overall length: 9.74 inches; Weight (unloaded with magazine): 2.2 lbs.; Barrel length: 6 inches; Magazine capacity: 5 (.38), 8 (.32), 10 (.22).

Specifications for P240 .22 LR: Overall length: 9.74 inches; Weight (unloaded with magazine): 2.2 lbs.; Barrel length: 6 inches; Magazine capacity: 10.

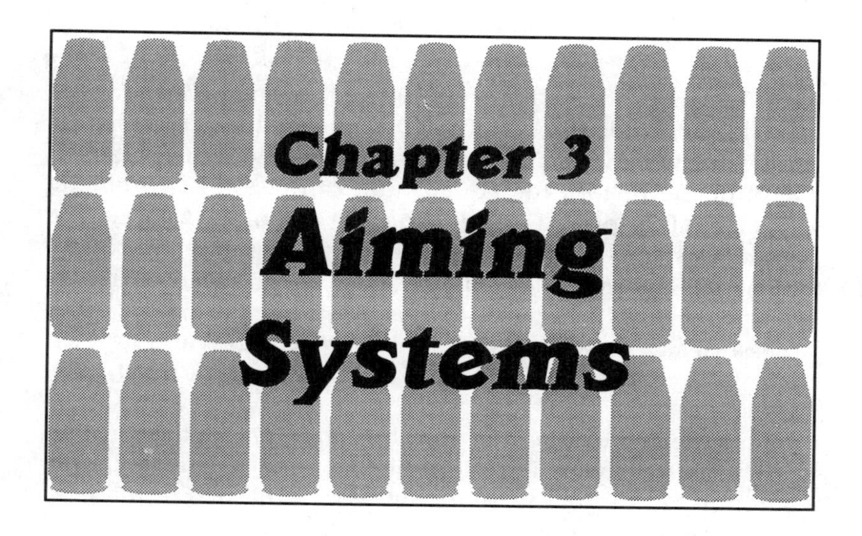

Chapter 3 Aiming Systems

The SIG, SIG-Sauer, and SIG-Hammerli pistols all have great potential accuracy right out of the box. Consequently, mounting quality sighting systems on these guns makes a lot of sense. Unfortunately, most of the SIG-Sauer guns currently in circulation are being used by police departments or government agencies interested only in the bare necessities on their pistols. For this reason, not a lot of scope mount systems are available for these fine guns, despite their potential for target and hunting use.

This will most likely change in the near future, especially in the gadget-conscious U. S. As the majority of the gun-owning population grows older and eyes are more farsighted, scopes become the best solution to getting a clear view of the target and sights. Consequently more sights are likely to spring up on all types of handguns as time goes by (provided the government doesn't ban the importation of these pistols—and at the time of this writing, there are unfortunate signs this may soon be done).

The great accuracy of the SIG-Sauer pistols also suggests that target shooters may soon be trading in their 1911 variants for more modern guns with a double-action trigger and better human engineering. Already there are a few customized SIG-Sauers showing up at ranges and contests around the world and it seems likely this trend will continue, too.

Whether a shooter adds a laser sight, optical scope, or even a flashlight to his pistol, there are some tradeoffs. While the additional weight isn't too great (and arguably reduces the felt recoil of the pistol), the added bulk can become a problem, especially if the pistol is to be carried for any time. And finding a good holster for a scoped or "lasered" handgun can be tough. But, as we'll see in the next chapter, manufacturers are currently working to supply the needs of those needing holsters and other accessories to go with pistols having specialized aiming gear mounted on them either above the slide or below the front of the frame.

This preamble out of the way, here are a few of the sighting systems currently available for the SIG pistol and its spinoffs. Undoubtedly more will soon come onto the marketplace as these guns gain in popularity.

Scopes and Scope Mounts

Iron sights on pistols are probably the best and cheapest solution to bringing a gun onto target for most shooters. While a telescopic sighting system appears quick once the gun is on target, getting it to that point isn't always that quick, due to the slight movements of a shooter's hand and the relatively narrow fields of view prevented by most scopes. Only with a lot of practice does scope sighting on a pistol become quick and reflexive.

For those who have shot and practiced with iron sights for many years, another problem shows up with scoped pistols; the gun is habitually raised to bring the iron sights to eye level, dictating a second motion to lower the gun a tad to align the eye with the scope. Because of this latter complication, many seasoned shooters find it takes a lot of extra practice before they can overcome old habits to bring a pistol on target with a scope as fast as they can with iron sights. These factors can cause critical extra moments before the crosshairs get on target if a shooter is unfamiliar with the scope system. Shooters shouldn't depend on a scoped pistol in the field or for self defense until aiming it has become a reflex.

A scope on a pistol also creates an added appendage on the

top of the firearm which dictates either a custom or competition holster. The latter opens a whole new range of problems since scopes are relatively fragile compared to iron sights; one drop or glancing blow may put a scope out of kilter or even destroy it. And of course the extra bulk of a scope on a pistol dictates more weight to be carried and lifted to target, not minor considerations for those carrying the pistol around all day or doing a lot of shooting at the range.

That said, some shooters, because of eye problems or other reasons, find iron sights almost impossible to use; these shooters will benefit from optical systems mounted on a pistol and are more than willing to put in the extra practice needed to rapidly acquire a target with a scope since it is an all or nothing proposition for these people when it comes to pistol shooting.

Of course once all that practice is put into aiming with a scope, it starts to show some important advantages. With optical scopes, the magnification makes identifying the target easier and may increase the shooter's accuracy as well in some cases. Furthermore, competition shooters have demonstrated that once a scope finally is mastered and the habit of bringing its aiming point up in front of the eye perfected, a scoped pistol can be much faster and more accurate than a gun having only iron sights, all other things being equal. For those willing to put in the practice and put up with the extra weight and frailties of a scope, there are some important edges to be gained.

Currently, while pistol scopes are abundant, scope mounts for the guns covered in this book aren't. Fortunately there are several good systems available for the P226 pistols. These mounts don't require any pistolsmithing and provide a rock solid mount for the standard Weaver rings that will accommodate most scopes.

Two styles of mounts for the P226 are offered by B-Square, a blued model (selling for $69.95) and a bright aluminum model that appears the same as stainless steel (selling for $79.95). The B-Square mounting system doesn't require gunsmithing work to mount the scope; all the shooter has to do is replace the takedown lever on the P226 with a cross-pin on the B-Square mount. This helps hold the mount securely in place along with the adjustment screws that bring the scope onto target. Should the shooter later want to remove the mount for some reason, the task is equally simple.

Aimpoint also offers a scope mount system for the P226. Available in black, this mount retails at $59.

For those wanting a less bulky scope mount that is also permanently attached to their SIG-Sauer, or for owners of models of SIG, SIG-Sauer, or SIG-Hammerli pistols which have no detachable scope mount available for them, the only solution is to hire a qualified gunsmith to make a custom mount. Fortunately this isn't as expensive a proposition as it once was, tbecause of the "race mounts" that have become widely available thanks to contest shooters. But none of these are actually "made to order" for any of the SIG, SIG-Sauer, or SIG-Hammerli pistols. Consequently a gunsmith will have to take a mount designed for another pistol and adapt it to the shooter's gun. While not excessively expensive, it nevertheless will require a lot of hand work and time—both of which translate into extra costs.

Permanent mounts also dictate drilling holes in the frame of the pistol to accommodate the attachment. With all of the guns covered in this book commanding hefty asking prices, careful thought should be given as to whether or not holes that might detract from or even ruin the collector's value and/or resale value of a firearm. Permanent scope mounts on a SIG, SIG-Sauer, or SIG-Hammerli pistol should be approached with caution and is work best left to a skilled gunsmith.

Once a shooter has a scope mount for his pistol, the next big decision is what type of scope to attach to it. Currently scopes fall into two broad categories, electric "dot" scopes and optical scopes.

There are two types of dot scopes: those operating on available light and those functioning with a small battery to produce a glowing dot via an LED (Light-Emitting Diode). Of the two, the battery-operated has become the most popular since the brightness of the dot can be adjusted according to the tastes of the shooter.

As most shooters know, most of today's competition shooters employ guns sporting electric "dot" scopes. The big advantage of this type of scope is that they permit aiming with both eyes open and have little if any parallax problems; while they're just as hard as other optical scopes to bring onto the bull's eye, shooters who practice extensively with these scopes can rapidly acquire a target. If speed is a shooter's goal, then the dot scope coupled with lots of practice is a good bet.

Another big plus dot scopes have over cross-hair optical scopes is that they can be used in the dark, producing a sight picture much like that of the laser—without giving away the shooter's presence to anyone in the target area since a dot scope, unlike a laser sight (more on these in a bit) which produces no indication of its presence to the front of the pistol. Dot scopes thus work not only during the day but at dusk or even nighttime for those using the firearm in self defense. This can be an important plus for many shooters.

Dot scopes have unlimited eye relief and don't suffer from any parallax problems; this allows a target to be accurately hit without placing the dot in the center of the field of view in the scope picture, an important plus for quick target acquisition and shooting. Most dot scopes display a tiny (usually red but sometimes green) ball of light in the center of the scope "picture."

While electric scopes are quick in acquiring targets, they aren't quick to turn on. It's generally necessary to twist a knob or, more rarely, throw a switch. Unfortunately no enterprising manufacturer has yet marketed a pressure switch similar to those described below which are common to laser sights or created a mercury switch that turns the scope on when the pistol is drawn from its holster. For this reason electric scopes should be turned on the moment a shooter expects to be shooting—an especially important point for those using these scopes for hunting or self defense. (Fortunately battery life is a number of hours for these scopes, making it possible to leave the scope on for extended time without fear of running down the battery—provided the battery is replaced on a regular basis.)

Among the best electric dot scopes currently available are those offered by Aimpoint, Action Arms, and Tasco. Tube size on the models offered by these companies varies; older 1-inch models are less expensive but give a narrower field of view than the newer 30mm or larger scopes do, making them less rapid in acquiring the target. Most shooters will discover they can acquire a target more rapidly if they purchase one of these larger scopes for their handgun.

On the other hand, in addition to costing less, the 1-inch tube scopes are also more compact. For those trying to carry a scoped gun in a holster, it makes a lot of sense to go with a 1-inch scope simply because it is smaller and therefore less apt to be bumped or damaged when being carried.

The Aimpoint 5000 offers a 30mm field of view. This scope is available in black matte or stainless finish, the scope can be powered by a pair of mercury SP675 batteries or, for cold weather use, a single lithium 2L76 or DL1/3N battery. The scope is 5.5 inches long and weighs 5.8 ounces; cost is $320. Since the 5000 scopes have tubes too large for one-inch Weaver rings, these are included with the scope and will accommodate most Weaver-style mounts.

[Photo courtesy of Aimpoint.]

Aimpoint's "Comp" scope is designed to capture a share of the competition shooting market. The 30mm field of view helps a shooter lock onto his target. Weight of the Comp scope is 4.75 ounces and the length is 4.365 inches. The scope comes with rings to permit easy mounting on Weaver rails.

Tasco offers the "ProPoint III" electric dot scope with a 30mm tube which gives a 25mm field of view. The scope comes with mounting rings and detachable sun shields that screw onto the front and/or rear of the scope. The ProPoint III comes in two versions, one with a small dot and the other with a "Big Dot" for faster target acquisition; both models cost $190.

Action Arms also offers a 30mm dot scope as their "Ultra Dot 30" which incorporates its battery pack into the small, click-adjustable brightness control knob, eliminating the cumbersome projecting battery pack seen on most other dot scope designs. The cost for the Ultra Dot 30 is $189; the scope is available in both stainless and matte black finishes.

Upping the ante a bit, Emerging Technologies recently introduced the "Laseraim Grand Illusion" which, despite its name, is a red dot scope. The Grand Illusion has a 50mm body that offers 300 percent more field of view than does a 1-inch scope, making it possible to "find" the dot more quickly than is the case with narrower dot scopes. It fits on standard Weaver bases without rings, thanks to integral claws mounted on it. The scope is available in both stainless and black finishes. ADCO currently offers the "Magnum 50mm" which is nearly identical to the Grand Illusion.

Recently several "tubeless" dot scopes have appeared on the market. These have the advantage of permitting the shooter to see the red dot on the mirrored lens at the front of the scope since it lacks a tube to block the view. This makes for quicker target acquisition and also a lighter sight. Of course the downside is that the sight is open, making it somewhat more sensitive to dirt than a sealed scope system. For those using the scope for self defense, it should also be noted that the LED may be somewhat visible from the side on some of these units, a potential tactical problem in a very dark environment.

Oddly enough, the tubeless system is based on an early 1900s-vintage shotgun sight. This design was resurrected in the 1970s by Daisy Air Rifles as a cheap plastic scope for air guns. Later, this design was modified with the addition of an LED (Light-Emitting Diode) and small electric watch battery so it would work in all types of light rather than just bright sunlight.

Since the patent has expired on the original design, several manufacturers have created more expensive versions of the open sight with a larger lens and 1-inch Weaver mounts, rather than the smaller 7/8-inch mounts common to air rifles and .22 rifles. But except for the larger field of view and sealed battery packs, these more expensive open sights are quite similar to those created by Daisy. Among the better of these "new" open tube sights designed for pistol mounting is the "C-More" which has proven to be popular with many competition shooters including IPSC World Champion (1993), Matt McLearn.

For those looking for an optical scope with traditional crosshairs and no electronics to contend with, a 1-power magnification scope is generally best for handguns since it permits aiming with both eyes open, giving the illusion of a wider field of view since the shooter's eyes combine the images from both eyes. However some shooters, especially hunters, may want some magnification; in such a case, a 2x, 3x, or even 4x power scope might be a more suitable choice than a 1x-power scope.

Tasco's "Proclass" pistol scopes are good picks for handgunners wanting an optical scope. This line of scopes comes in a variety of powers and reticles and have 30mm tubes that give longer eye relief and a greater field of view. The scopes come with 30mm rings so mating them to standard-sized Weaver mounts like those mentioned above is simple.

Tall shooters considering the purchase of a cross-hair optical scope should always check for adequate eye relief (the distance from the eye to the scope) before they make any purchases; a few optical cross-hair scopes don't have long enough eye relief for those with longer arms. Also it's a good idea to purchase a name brand scope like Bushnell, Tasco, or others to insure quality of the optics as well as repair of the scope if it is ever damaged. Bargain scopes with little-known names are almost always iffy at best and a waste of money when they go haywire.

Whether you choose an electric dot scope or an optical scope, it's important to put in extensive practice with it. This makes it possible to quickly bring the pistol onto its intended target without having to "hunt" around for it.

Sights

If a shooter has good eyesight, arguably the best sights for the SIG, SIG-Sauer, and SIG-Hammerli pistols are the ones the guns come with. These sights have been carefully designed, fit the guns perfectly, and are generally best suited to the tasks the gun will be employed for.

Standard SIG-Sauer sights [Photo courtesy of Sigarms.]

Sig Lite sights with tritium inserts. [Photo courtesy of Sigarms.]

Since the majority of gunfights occur at night or in poorly lit areas, "SIG Lite", glow-in-the-dark make a lot of sense because they assist in locating a target in dim light. Like most modern night sights, these contain small glass vials of tritium gas (an isotope of hydrogen); these tiny containers are inserted into small holes drilled in the front and rear sights. Tritium sights give a bright glowing point of light that is easily aligned with a target in the darkest of environments. The life of the radioactive material is such that the dots will remain bright and useable at night for at least 10 years before they need to be replaced.

Radioactive things make most of us a bit squirmy. But tritium is very safe since no radiation other than visible light penetrates the glass vial containing the radioactive gas. And even if a vial of a tritium sight breaks indoors—an occurrence that is hard to imagine unless the sight were abused—the exposure to radiation is minimal since the gas quickly dissipates into the atmosphere (though to be on the safe side, the room should be aired out if such an accident chances to occur).

There is a huge variety of aftermarket sights available for the SIG-Sauer pistols with relatively few being available for the others; probably the best source for these is Brownells which has most of the sights in stock and is just a phone call away for those with plastic charge cards.

Wayne Novak has created a "Carry" rear sight for the SIG-Sauer guns. The sights are rounded to make them snag free and have a large, rebated sight notch for a clear picture of the target. Cost is $30 for a standard black rear sight with a two-white-dot sight costing $35 from Brownells.

Millett adjustable rear sights are available for the SIG-Sauer P220, P225, and P226; all require a companion front sight. The rear sights are adjustable both for elevation and windage with miniature screws located on the sight. The Millett rear sight blade is available in one of three choices including a target, white outline, or 2-dot configuration; cost is $55.60 for any of these three styles for any of the above guns. The required front sights are available in white, orange, dot, and black serrated styles for the P220 (cost is $16 each). With the P225 and P226, white, orange, or a dot style front sights are available, also for $16.

Millett also offers adjustable glow-in-the-dark tritium night sights for the SIG-Sauer P225, P226, and both the old and new style P220. These cost $135 per set of front and rear sights. Like the standard Millett sights, the rear sight is adjustable for both windage and elevation.

Pachmayr offers an adjustable rear sight for the SIG-Sauer P220, P225, P226, and P228. The sight is available in a target, white outline, and 3-dot configuration and is adjustable for elevation and windage. The price, $67.

One of the first manufacturers to create a night sight for military, police, and civilian use was Trijicon. Not surprisingly then, Trijicon offers sights for all models of the SIG-Sauer pistols with the plus of having an adjustable rear sight. Cost is $175 per set. Trijicon also offers fixed sights for all SIG-Sauer pistols; these carry a price tag of $115 per set.

Israeli Military Industries has developed a similar series of tritium sights for a variety of its firearms. The U. S. distributor, Hesco, Inc., markets these as the "Meprolight" sights and they fit the SIG-Sauer P220, P225, P226, and P228. Cost is $95 per set.

Whether night sights are used on a pistol or standard iron sights, they aren't of much use if not properly zeroed. Fortunately the sights on most of the SIG and SIG-Sauer pistols will have been zeroed at the factory and shouldn't be adjusted unless, for some reason, they are not on the mark. If this latter situation is the case, the sights are easily adjusted for windage and—with a bit of labor—for elevation. Before zeroing, it's wise to choose the type of ammunition that will most often be fired from the gun and zero the sights with that ammunition to avoid the changes that can occur when switching from one type of ammunition to another.

With a pistol that shoots low and has non-adjustable sights, the rule is to "lower" the front sight by removing metal from its top to raise the group. If the pistol shoots high, filing the rear sight's notch and top edge will lower the group. Obviously this work needs to be done cautiously since once the metal is removed, it's really tough to put it back. It's wise to have a gunsmith handle the task, though most do-it-yourselfers can tackle the job with some success.

Guns having sights that can be adjusted for elevation make zeroing an easier task. The rule with these is to raise the rear sight to raise the group and lower the sight to lower the group-pretty simple and hard to confuse. To help out, most adjustable sights will be marked with an "E" for elevation and an arrow showing the "UP" direction needed to raise groups.

SIG-Sauer rear sight adjustment tool. [Photo courtesy of Sigarms.]

Bullet impact can be "moved" to one side slightly by drifting the rear sight; on SIG-Sauer guns, this is best done with the company's rear sight adjustment tool, though a drift punch or wooden peg placed against the sight and lightly tapped with a hammer will work. When adjusting the windage of such sights, the rear sight should be moved opposite to the direction of the change in impact desired; if, for example, the pistol shoots to the right of the point of aim, the rear sight should be drifted to the left.

With adjustable sights, moving the sight to the left moves the point of aim to the right (shifting groups to the left); moving the rear sight to the left moves the groups to the right. Usually the sight will be marked with an "L" or "R" to show which way to turn the micrometer screw to shift the group.

Lasers

The tight beam of coherent light from a laser moves in a straight line while a bullet's path is a shallow arch due to gravity and air resistance. But despite the difference between the straight line of light and the trajectory of a bullet, both are close enough within several hundred yards to keep them within a few inches of each other when both are properly aligned. This makes a laser a practical aiming device within the useful range of any of the pistols covered in this book.

Modern laser sights have elevation and windage screws much like those of optical scopes; this makes zeroing them to a pistol simple. The shooter employs the pistol's iron sights to aim at the target, turns on the laser, and notes where its beam strikes on the target, adjusting the laser accordingly until its beam hits at the same point as the iron sights target.

Like everything else, lasers do have some disadvantages, especially in combat since the laser can be readily seen by an opponent. And in the daylight, most lasers aren't bright enough to be seen unless used with special targets—though this may be changing as we'll see in a moment. All of this means that lasers are only practical for self defense in very limited conditions, currently either indoors or during dusk and the night.

It's also important to note that laser sights aren't suited to group use by military or police squads, except when only the "leader" has a laser and uses it to direct the fire of his team. Otherwise, if each person in a squad has a laser sight, it becomes almost impossible in combat to tell which aiming point belongs to whom.

Care has to be exercised with laser sights. But within ideal operating environments, such a sight on a SIG or SIG-Sauer pistol can be very effective and fast in bringing the firearm onto target. Too, a shooter doesn't need to bring his pistol to eye level and can fire with both eyes wide open without fear of an inaccurate shot with a laser sight. All he has to do is place the laser dot on the target, keep the firearm steady, and fire.

Hollywood has also given laser sight users an additional plus. Because heroes in action movies often have laser sights—and almost never miss the target —the intimidation factor of a laser sight is currently great. Almost no one is going to stand still once a laser starts to flickering at them.

For years seasoned gunfighters have known that most people cower when being shot at; simply firing quickly and *then* taking careful aim often gives a shooter a chance to get a clear second shot at an opponent who is too busy ducking from the initial report to aim. Much the same thing happens with the laser sight; an opponent starts to duck for cover rather than returning aimed fire. The added plus is that no ammunition is wasted by the laser user as he brings his weapon on target.

Of course a laser sight isn't going to make everyone cower in terror. And as more combatants get used to seeing these sights in action, and realize that they aren't necessarily more accurate than standard sights, especially if the shooter hasn't practiced much with them, then the intimidation factor is going to drop off. But in the meantime, it's something to keep in mind and exploit if you have a laser mounted on a defensive arm.

Until recently, laser sights were too large to fit easily on pistols. But that has changed over the last few years with the introduction of solid-state lasers that were originally designed for compact disc players. When these came out in the 1980s, designers in the firearms industry were soon incorporating the new gadgets into compact, tough sighting systems that were finally small enough to mount on pistols. Today there are a number of compact laser sights and mounts for the Sig, SIG-Sauer, and, if one so desires, SIG-Hammerli pistols.

Commercial laser sights are limited in power by the U. S. Federal Government to prevent potential damage to a user's eyes with 5 milliwatts being the maximum. But that's all the power needed since a 5-milliwatt laser produces a dot that can be readily seen in dim light for several hundred yards—farther than the useful range of pistols. Range isn't the only factor to consider, however. While less powerful laser sights work well, many pistol shooters have opted to use full-power 5-milliwatt laser sights because the brighter beam is more easily seen in areas bordering on daylight. The larger 5 milliwatt laser sight makes the laser sight practical in brighter environments.

The reason lasers aren't readily visible in daylight is complicated, but basically boils down to the fact that the red wavelength is too long to remain easily detectable by the human eye once the pupils adjust to sunlight. But part of the problem is more than wavelength; a 5mw laser is too dim to show up in bright sunlight, regardless of its wavelength.

Nevertheless, several manufacturers have recently introduced a "day" laser sight that shortens the wavelength down from the standard 670 nm (nanometer) wavelength of most lasers to 635 nm. While the result of a shorter wave isn't exactly brilliant in sunlight, it is visible under conditions when the standard 670 nm lasers are invisible and when shining on a reflective surface, can be seen even in sunlight, making it possible to sight the pistol in during the day if special reflective targets are exploited (these targets are available from most manufacturers offering 635nm lasers). If the trend toward shorter wavelength lasers were to continue, the limitation of these sights to use only in very dark environments might be less of a consideration, though it's doubtful that any laser with only 5mw of power will be visible in bright sunlight at any great range.

Infrared laser sights have also been introduced for military and police users. These have the added advantage of being only visible to users wearing night vision goggles. These lasers can be left on and permit careful aiming without detection—provided an opponent isn't also wearing night vision goggles. (For a more detailed look at laser aiming devices as well as night vision gear, see *Laser Sights and Night Vision Devices*, available from Desert Publications for $29.95.)

Battery life varies according to the power of the laser sight and size of the battery supply, but most 3 milliwatt lasers will last up to 50 hours of continuous use before they need new batteries, while full-power lasers generally wear out batteries considerably sooner. Full-power 5 milliwatt lasers have considerably shorter battery life.

Since the beam of a laser sight is readily noticeable when it's in operation, good tactical use of the laser dictates only switching it on long enough to acquire the target and fire. To do this, a momentary switch is used with most laser sights with the switch mounted on the grip of the pistol.

That said, a few laser sights are marketed with only an on/off switch; this has the plus of doing away with the awkward wire connecting momentary switches to their lasers, but shooters must learn to aim their pistol straight down or into the air after firing to avoid having the beam give away their position to their target when he returns fire. (It should also be noted that laser beams are especially noticeable in smoke, fog, or rain so great care must be exercised with these sights in combat environments like these.)

The momentary switch on lasers creates a few problems when mounting the system on a pistol. If care isn't taken, the wire connecting the switch to the laser can stick out, potentially ready to snarl in brush, or extend into the slide area of the pistol, creating the possibility of a jam at a critical moment. For this reason many shooters carry on a love/hate relationship with the momentary switch and its wire, trying to get the cable to remain untangled.

For this reason, some shooters opt for a standard off/on switch on the laser, even though it has the tactical disadvantages mentioned above. Others try to tape the switch to the grip of the gun, discovering the hard way that most tape oozes its adhesive over time or dissolves in cleaning solvents, creating a sticky mess on the firearm.

One viable solution to the problem is to use black wire wraps (similar to those used on bread wrappers) to tie the cable to the underside of the trigger guard and then mount the momentary switch to the grip with Superglue. More permanent mounts can be created with epoxy putty—at the risk of damaging the gun when the assembly has to be removed for one reason or another. A few shooters have even experimented with large black rubber "O" ring washers and rubber bands with varying results. With experimentation most shooters eventually come up with a solution, though it seems that no really good system of mounting the momentary switch on the pistol grip at a convenient location without having wires or fasteners protrude from the firearm.

For a time one company marketed a "wireless" switch that employed low-power radio waves to activate the laser sight. This permitted gluing or otherwise fastening the switch in place on the grip without any need for a connecting cable. This system has run into a few snags of its own, however. Hopefully the bugs will be worked out of the system to create a viable alternative to toggle and cable-attached momentary switches in the near future.

As for the various models currently available, perhaps the handiest laser sight to date for the SIG-Sauer pistols is the B-Square "Mini-Laser" which boasts a full 5 milliwatt of power in a compact size, only 1.1-inch square by a half inch, and a light weight of only a tad over 1 ounce *with* its batteries and remote switch. This laser attaches to any of the SIG-Sauer pistols with a universal mount that fits around the trigger guard.

The Mini-Laser is available in blued or stainless finish models with a choice of either an on/off switch that mounts on the laser just ahead of the trigger guard or a momentary switch on a cord. In addition to its compact size, the Mini-Laser has several added pluses. One is that it can be easily removed from its mount thanks to locking detentes; it's also possible to replace the batteries in the sight without removing it from the gun. These two design features make for a very flexible system. Cost is $300 for a blued Mini-Laser with cord or switch and $309 for the stainless model.

TacStar offers excellent lasers including the Tac-Star "Universal Pistol Laser" and "T2000" which are ideal for mounting on pistols. These laser sights are operated by a remote pressure switch. The "T2000" will accept an optional rotary switch that fastens to the base of the laser for easy off/on selection with the trigger finger.

The "Universal Pistol Laser" is 2.44 inches long by .550 inch in diameter and weighs 1.2 ounces including its lithium battery. Its body is constructed of 6061 aluminum with a choice of black or clear (stainless) anodized finish; cost is $99. It comes with polymer inserts for its universal mount that enables a correct fit to SIG-Sauer P220, P226, and P228 guns.

TacStar's T-2000 is an extremely small laser sight scarcely larger than a .45 ACP cartridge, measuring 1.5 inches long and .55 inches in diameter; weight with batteries is only one ounce. The T-2000 comes in a choice of blued or stainless finishes; cost is $235.

The Universal Pistol Laser features a universal mount. [Photo courtesy of TacStar Industries.]

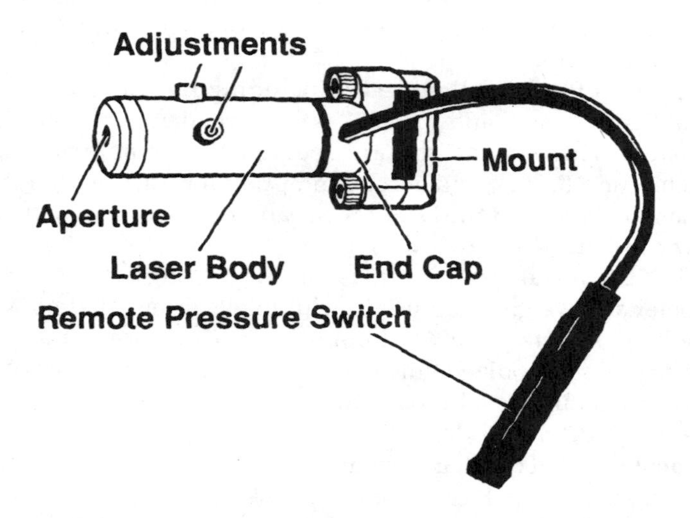

Components of the Universal Pistol Laser. [Photo courtesy of TacStar Industries.]

It can be attached to a SIG or SIG-Sauer pistol with TacStar's new "Universal Pistol Mount". The sight is held to the mount with a clamp making it easy to attach/dis-attach the T-2000 to or from the pistol with just an "L" wrench.

The T2000 exhibits the same physical characteristics as this discontinued T-1000 shown on a problematic "glue on" mount. [Photo courtesy of TacStar Industries.]

Discontinued T-1000 shown with finger-activated rotary switch; the T2000 also has this optional rotary switch. [Photo courtesy of TacStar Industries.]

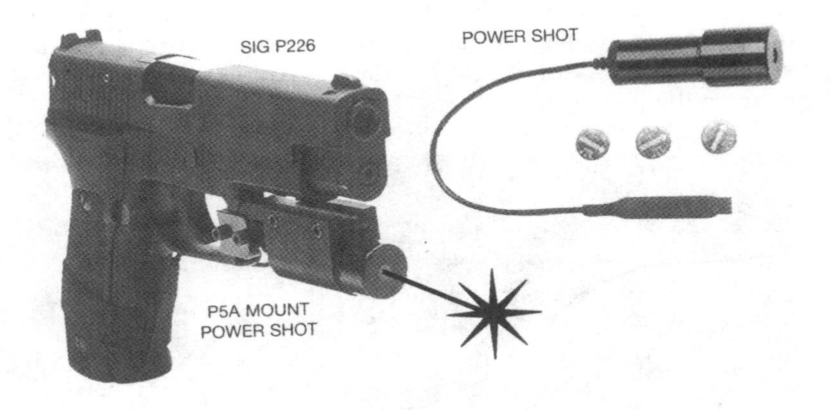

Power Shot laser sight mounted on P226 (left). Powershot laser with batteries (right). [Photo courtesy of ALPEC Team, Inc.]

ALPEC also a standard (i.e., night only) laser sight dubbed the "Laser Shot" which also uses a trigger guard mount; included in this group of mounts are those designed for many of the SIG-Sauer pistols. The Laser Shot is .75 inch in diameter and 2.625 inches long, weighing 3 ounces (including the battery and mount). Cost is $105 plus the cost of the mount (running $21 to $26).

ALS (Applied Laser Systems) offers the "Miniaimer" series of lasers with two wavelengths being available, one in 670nm and the other in 635nm. These laser sights are available in blued and stainless finishes with a mount that attaches to the trigger guard of a P220, P225, P226, or P228. Mounts cost $52 with the

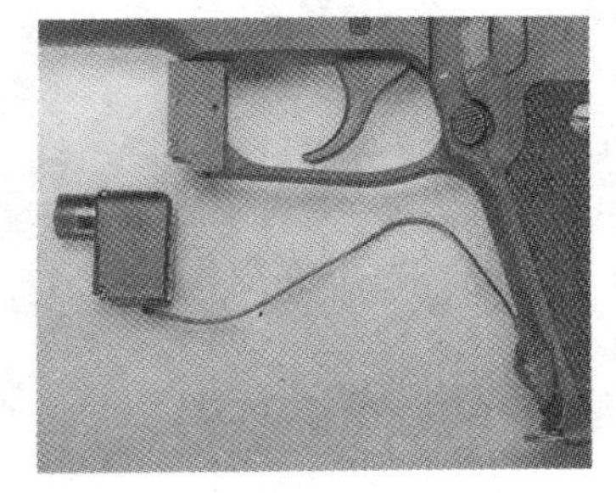

Miniaimer, shown in detached position with mount attached to trigger guard. [Photo courtesy of ALS.]

670nm laser running $246 while the "day" MiniAimer (with a shorter 635nm wavelength) runs at $350.

Regardless of the brand of laser mounted on a pistol, the laser is not a magical device that makes every bullet reach the exact spot the shooter was aiming for. To achieve accuracy with a laser sight, a shooter must practice and learn to hold his firearm steady and on target during the full pull of the trigger.

Flashlights and Flashlight Mounts

Just as laser sights have recently "shrunk" thanks to technology, so, too, has the flashlight, with krypton or other gases making a considerably brighter but more compact bulb possible and new battery systems making the overall size of flashlights small as well. As the size has decreased and the brightness increased, some shooters have discovered that placing a very compact, high-intensity light on a pistol makes sense given the fact that the majority of shootouts occur in darkened conditions. A flashlight on a pistol helps the shooter determine who is friend or foe—something that can't easily be done with iron sights having tritium inserts or with a laser sight. Since innocent bystanders or family members can be in areas that may be invaded by a criminal, a bright flashlight can not only identify a target, it can be a lifesaver by giving the user quick visual confirmation of his target.

When a flashlight is aligned with the barrel of a pistol, the light can also serve as an aiming device, making it practical to ignore the sights when engaging a criminal at very close range. At longer ranges, the light will silhouette the iron sights, making possible targeting for very accurate shots in otherwise dark environments.

Some flashlights even produce enough light to dazzle a criminal in the process of identifying him, giving the user a slight advantage over him. (Carrying this process to its extreme, the U. S. National Institute of Justice is currently working with the Lawrence Livermore National Laboratory to produce a bright electronic strobe that pulses rapidly in coordination with special visors worn by the law officers using the strobe. The goggles become almost opaque when the strobe flashes, then instantly become transparent when it is off, both processes taking place very swiftly. When perfected, this will make it possible to bathe an area with light, blinding a suspect while the law enforcement personnel wearing the visors will be able to see normally when the light is in its off mode. Whether or not this system can be "shrunk" to the point it would permit pistol mounting remains to be seen, however.)

Of course a flashlight shows exactly where the shooter is and makes a dandy target. So care has to be exercised with these devices, even when they're mounted on a firearm as a sighting system. As with the laser sight, it's important to only shine a flashlight for brief periods, then move to another location quickly in the darkness. To employ such tactics, a momentary switch that can be easily activated is a must for a flashlight mounted on a pistol.

Flashlights also have a limited "range," quickly spreading out over any distance. Therefore flashlight "sights" are effective only with targets within 10 or 20 yards of the shooter with the advantage of the light quickly becoming a liability at greater ranges.

The added bulk of a flashlight on a pistol can also create problems, though it can also act to reduce felt recoil. And of course holster carry becomes almost impossible with some flashlight mounts (though newer, small flashlights can fit into holsters designed for laser-equipped pistols).

Currently the most ideal flashlight system for mounting on a SIG-Sauer pistol is the "MicroStar T-45" flashlight offered by TacStar Industries. This bright flashlight is machined from 6061 T6 aluminum and has a black or "stainless" anodized finish and operates on three AAAA batteries which are readily available in most areas of the world. A momentary remote switch can be attached to the pistol grip for rapidly switching the light on and off; the switch can be secured anywhere on the grip with a Velcro strip supplied with the MicroStar.

Mounting the MicroStar to any of the SIG-Sauer pistols is a snap since TacStar Industries has designed the flashlight to fit its laser mounts. Cost of the MicroStar is $40 for either a black or stainless finish; the "Laser Pistol Mount" which joins the flashlight to a SIG-Sauer pistol costs an additional $40 (and is also available in both stainless steel and black finish). This combination gives the buyer a very useful nighttime "tool" for his pistol for just $80.

MicroStar EMLM mount with MicroStar flashlight. [Photo courtesy of TacStar Industries.]

TacStar Industries also has a "MicroStar EMLM" mount that mates the company's MicroStar flashlight to a SIG-Sauer 20-round 9mm magazine. The big plus of this system is that the flashlight can be added to or removed from the gun with just a magazine exchange; it also permits a flashlight being added to a gun already having an under-the-barrel laser mounted on it. Of course the downside is that once the magazine is exhausted, the flashlight leaves the pistol during a reload. But since most gunfights are over with just a few shots, this doesn't present too much of a problem except in rare cases. The mount accommodates standard mini-AA flashlights as well as the MicroStar. Cost is $35.

Regardless of the flashlight mount a shooter uses, as with other systems careful practice is essential. A shooter should be able to use the light almost instinctively to illuminate his target, fire if necessary, and then avoid possible return fire by switching the light off and quickly moving to another position. Otherwise the shooter may experience a "terminal" failure of his tactics.

Due to the high price tags on the SIG and SIG-Sauer guns, as well as the fact that these pistols are often employed "bare bones" by military, government, and police agents, there aren't as many accessories, bells, and whistles available for these pistols as one might expect. This is especially true when comparing the SIG and SIG-Sauer to more popular pistols like the TZ/CZ-75 series of pistols or the venerable Colt 1911 and its spinoffs.

This isn't all bad, however, because many of the gadgets presently sold for pistols don't do a lot to improve the functioning of the firearm and a few lower the reliability of pistols—with disastrous results if the firearm is being used for self-protection. In fact, most shooters are better off purchasing quality ammunition and then devoting their time in perfecting shooting skills rather than buying the latest gadgety add-on for their pistol. The fact that the SIG and SIG-Sauer pistols have fewer accessories than some other guns may actually be more of a plus than a minus, all things considered.

Olin/Winchester, Action Ammo, Federal Cartridge Company, Omark/CCI, Remington, Black Hills Ammunition, and PMC are among the manufacturers that offer quality ammunition that is non-corrosive (unlike some of the surplus and Eastern-European ammunition that still occasionally shows up on the marketplace). When it comes to accuracy, these companies have excellent match grade ammunition that allows a shooter to take full advantage of the precision shooting offered by these pistols. For extended practice, PMC, Winchester, and Federal all offer low-cost "generic" ammunition.

For those firing the SIG-Hammerli in .22 LR or the SIG or SIG-Sauers with a .22 LR adapter, Federal's new .22 match ammunition is hard to beat (though all of those wanting to achieve the greatest accuracy should experiment with ammunition from a variety of companies). If one of these pistols is called upon to dispatch varmints, then great results can be had with CCI's .22 LR "Stinger" ammunition which packs a punch that drops small rodents in their tracks. And for super quiet, short-range practice, Remington, CCI, and Federal all offer ".22 CB Caps", ammunition built around a .22 LR case but with less power than a .22 Short and a lighter bullet than the standard .22 LR, making the report of the gun relatively soft when using these rounds indoors or even in the back yard (local laws permitting, of course). About the only downside to this ammunition is that its low power requires hand cycling between shots—and even this can be a plus for those teaching a beginner.

The majority of SIG, SIG-Sauer, and SIG-Hammerli owners find that all they need is their pistol and quality ammunition for great shooting; they don't need the latest dohickies, grips, and gadgets. Practice does the trick.

Of course for some there are a few gadgets that can be worth their weight in gold. Anyone who's faced an opponent in the darkness can appreciate a good set of tritium night sights or a laser sight like those covered in the previous chapter for dealing with a criminal who is only a dark shadow. And for those wanting to enter competition, then a "comp gun" modification of a SIG-Sauer might be called for, with the magazine bumper pads, special grips, sights, and maybe even porting or a custom compensator similar to that other contestants will be using to gain each incremental advantage they can over their fellow contestants. In such a case, accessories and replacement parts are a necessity, at least in the eyes of the competition shooter.

But care must be taken in adding even quality accessories to a pistol. Things can, and do, go wrong. Adding a laser sight will most likely make it impossible to use the "perfect" holster a shooter purchased earlier on. The new holster purchased to accommodate the laser sight may cause the pistol to interfere with a ballistic vest or permit the butt of a rifle to smack against it, raising noise that gives away a SWAT team member's position. Likewise new grips purchased to give added control of a SIG-Sauer may make it impossible to work the magazine release without repositioning the hand.

And on it goes.

The wrong mix of the best of guns and accessories can create headaches and perhaps even life-threatening handicaps. To avoid such problems, anyone who plays "mix and match" with a pistol and accessories for it needs to be careful to test each new configuration carefully to be certain that nothing can go wrong at a critical moment.

Carrying Cases

Collectors should always keep the boxes they purchase their firearms in, especially with the high-ticket guns covered in this book. Storing a pistol in the box it came in can also be wise since the boxes are constructed to minimize the chances of damage from moisture (provided they're kept in a relatively dry environment). If the owner takes the time to oil the firearm from time to time, it should last indefinitely, especially in the case of stainless steel and alloy frame SIG-Sauer models.

SIG-Sauer's hard plastic case is ideal for storage and even transport of the company's pistols. The foam padding inside the case and the hard plastic exterior give the firearm a maximum of protection.

For those interested in shooting their pistol on a regular basis, moving the gun in and out of a box will quickly wear out the box and do little for the shooter's patience. In such a situation, a gun carrying case is ideal both for storing and transporting the pistol since it will protect the firearm from bumps and scratches as well as from rust and dirt. A case can also be employed for long-term storage of a firearm.

SIG-Sauer pistol case is ideal for carrying or storing a pistol. [Photo courtesy of Sigarms.]

With both blued steel and stainless steel/alloy frame firearms, it's important to avoid using a plastic bag, vinyl pouch, or other sealed container for a storage case since these promote rust and tarnishing because air can't flow through the container. With stainless steel guns an airtight case will eventually cause severe discoloration and blued sights will develop major areas of rust; blued guns will quickly rust in such containers. For this reason, a burlap-weave pistol "rug" is a must because it will permit moisture to escape from around the gun, heading off a lot of potential problems with rust.

One excellent source for such cases is Michaels of Oregon whose Uncle Mike's "Sidekick Pistol Rugs" are sold in most gun stores. The thick Cordura nylon padded foam cases have a brushed lining that won't damage the finish on a pistol. These rugs come in assorted colors including black, tan, camouflage, and forest green with the small size rug being ideal for the SIG-Sauer P230 and the medium size fitting most of the other models covered in this manual. Cost is $12 per rug.

Compensators, Ports, and Muzzle Brakes

Although compensators, ports, and muzzle brakes are most often seen on contest guns, more and more appear on "carry" guns these days and it seems likely that this trend will continue. Technically a compensator or gas port prevents the upward climb of the muzzle during recoil while a muzzle brake reduces felt recoil. But most of these devices actually counter both recoil and muzzle flip to varying extents. The benefits of these devices include both more comfort and quicker, accurate shooting since the sights can be brought back onto target more quickly after a shot is fired due to reduced barrel rise. On the downside, many compensators add weight to a firearm and some add length as well. This latter point often dictates the purchase of new holsters to accommodate the added length and any such pistol is going to be a bit more fatiguing to carry for long periods of time.

Compensators are not all that new. John Moses Browning was using diverted gas to power his early machine gun designs in the late 1800s and the first Thompson submachine guns of the 1920s sported Cutts compensators. But the current craze for compensated pistols can be traced to the 1970s when these devices started showing up on IPSCC guns where contestants employed compensators to help bring the muzzle of their pistols back onto target in a hurry, a prime requisite for winning contests.

These first compensators were simply ports cut into barrels which extended an inch beyond the slide of the automatic. But soon the portion of the barrel extending beyond the slide was being encased in a muzzle weight for greater recoil reduction due to the inertia of the added weight; most of these compensators were simply a cylinder-shaped weight, often with ports, wrapped around the extended barrel. But soon more aesthetically pleasing "full-profile" compensators were appearing; these followed the contours of the slide, blending with its lines.

During this same period some shooters were adding weights to the front of the frame below the slide, often with a solid block of steel being welded to the front of the frame, creating a massive assembly toward the front of the gun. Like the weight of the compensators attached to barrels, this added weight fights against the recoil of the gun. Whether below the frame or on the barrel, as long as the added mass isn't on the slide, the "lock time" (the period of time before the barrel disengages from the slide, ejects an empty cartridge, and then rechambers a round and locks up the action) doesn't become greater (as it would if the weight were added to the slide). This means that added weight not attached to the slide translates into a gun that can be fired more rapidly. Of course the downside to this is a much heavier gun—a pain if one has to carry the gun for long.

The latest trick gunsmiths use with more sophisticated compensators is an "expanding chamber" next to the muzzle of the barrel followed by a narrowed exit hole for the bullet. Gas becomes compressed behind the bullet and exits the compensation slots with greater pressure, thereby increasing the downward deflection that operates against the muzzle rise. Gas pressure against the narrow exit hole of the compensator also reduces felt recoil in this design.

Another has nothing to do with added weights or the porting of gas. Instead this system changes the power of the recoil spring to modify the rearward travel of the slide. If done properly, this can prevent the slide from banging abruptly against the frame at its rear-most position and thereby spread out the recoil force of the pistol so it can be controlled more easily by the shooter. There are currently two ways to achieve this. One is with a progressive rate recoil spring which changes its tension as it is compressed; the other is to place a powerful secondary spring inside the recoil guide where it will be engaged only during the last inch of the recoil cycle.

Because of the very small numbers of SIG and SIG-Sauer pistols that are used in contest shooting, the only compensators available for these guns are those built on a custom basis. These command big bucks since the work dictates a lot of machining and careful fitting of parts.

There is one other solution for those wanting a compensated SIG or SIG-Sauer, however. This is to drop back to the original design that ported gas through the barrel and cuts in the slide. The best-known of the companies doing such work is Mag-na-port International, which uses a special process developed for NASA that beams electrons, "knocking away" tiny sections of metal. This system produces very smooth port openings with no damage to the surface of the metal as the ports are cut into the slide and barrel of a pistol.

Mag-na-porting can be done through both the slide and the barrel of a SIG or SIG-Sauer since both are locked together during the major part of the recoil cycle; this has the added benefit of leaving the profile and length of the gun the same and is relatively inexpensive. About the only drawback with extended shooting is a bit of fouling being left behind inside the slide and frame from gas that leaks into this area. Most shooters find this a worthwhile trade off since the Mag-na-ports are effective in reducing both muzzle rise and felt recoil, especially with the 9mm, .40 S&W, and .357 SIG. Cost for modification of a pistol is $90 plus shipping (usually around $5 per slide); those interested in this work should first contact Mag-na-port for shipping instructions.

It should be noted that when some types of accessories are added to the frame of a pistol, they'll help compensate for recoil through their added mass. For example, adding a flashlight or one of the larger lasers listed in the previous chapter will increase the mass of the firearm and compensate to some extent for muzzle rise—a point worth considering when picking out bolt-on accessories.

Ear and Eye Protection

Of course a shooter can't stop in the middle of a gun fight and don his ear and eye protection—though it is rumored that some of the submachine gun-toting hoods of the Roaring Twenties regularly stuffed their ears with cotton before snuffing a foe with bullets. But whenever ear and eye protection can be used, they not only help prevent hearing loss and damage to the eyes, they also help keep flinches and other noise-inspired bad shooting habits from developing. Shooting without ear and eye protection is asking for trouble in one form or another.

Ear muffs and ear plugs are readily accessible from almost any gun shop. For those who wish to shop by mail, Brigade Quartermasters sells the excellent "Earsaf" ear muffs for $13 and GI ear plugs for $3. These must be used properly for maximum effectiveness. Most shooters don't insert expanding ear plugs deep enough into the ear canal; the secret is to roll the foam into a tight rod and then insert it far into the ear before it starts to expand.

Totally gross but effective "expedient ear plugs" can be created by chewing on a couple of strips of Kleenex and then stuffing the chunks of wet paper into the ears. This isn't sanitary and can cause ear infections since it gets moisture and bacteria from the mouth into the ears. But it works and is better than nothing for shooters who forget ear protectors and who happen to have a Kleenex in their pocket.

The most ideal shooting glasses are made of coated polycarbonate are both durable and tough, capable of stopping shotgun pellets or other slow-moving projectiles, therefore making them suitable for combat use as well as for practice. Among the best of these are the wrap-around, stylish Gargoyles from Brigade Quartermasters; these are sold in clear, yellow, vermillion, bronze, and lunar grey for $65 each. Mirrored models are marketed as well including full mirrored or a gradient mirror finish for $75 per pair; 18KT gold models of the Gargoyles sell for from $80 to $160.

Brigade Quartermasters also offers the "Ski Optiks" line of regular polycarbonate glasses; these don't give quite as much eye protection since they don't wrap around the side of the face but they are effective. Cost for the mirrored amber or blue models is $45 while the standard grey glasses run $49 a pair. Stylish polycarbonate glasses are also offered by companies like Jones Optical and Ame. However purchasers must always double check that the plastic used for the glasses is polycarbonate and that it's treated to give ultraviolet protection; non-polycarbonate glasses don't offer nearly as much eye protection.

For those wanting to save a bit of cash, shooting glasses or safety goggles designed for protection when using power tools can often be purchased in sporting and hardware stores for considerably less than $20—and sometimes for as little as $10. Care must be taken to be sure these glasses are made of polycarbonate and–if shooting is done outdoors–that they offer protection from ultraviolet light; otherwise the glasses may do more harm than good.

Brigade Quartermasters offers another useful training product, "Low Lites" goggles. These are like super-dark sunglasses. Shooters wearing these see things around them in daylight the way everything would appear at night or in dim light. Since most gunfights take place in poor light, police units and other groups often practice with these goggles to get the feel of tactics and equipment in darkness; such rehearsals often point out the need for different tactics and equipment and help insure success when team members operate at night. Low Lites are available from Brigade Quartermasters for $10 a pair.

Grip Panels

The SIG and SIG-Sauer wrap-around grip panels have been carefully designed and are well liked by most shooters. Consequently the majority of shooters are best advised to leave well enough alone on these guns, perhaps opting for the SIG-Sauer optional walnut grips if they wish to "fancy up" their pistols.

Of course some shooters prefer a "rubberized" grip to wood or plastic. And there are several companies which offer such aftermarket grips for the SIG-Sauer guns. Shooters desiring these grips feel that the rubber adds a little flex during recoil, reducing its effects somewhat. Many also like the added traction the rubber gives, making a hold more secure. On the flip side, some shooters dislike this added friction since it makes it harder to alter the placement of the hand on the pistol if it is drawn with a poor hand positioning. (These grips also have a slight intimidation factor; criminals often avoid trouble with policemen having rubberized replacement grips on their firearms since the grips are often a mark of a shooter who is familiar with his firearm and a crack shot.)

Most of these grips have a black, soft rubber exterior with a nylon insert that fits into the frame of the pistol for added strength.

SIG-Sauer optional wooden grips. [Photo courtesy of Sigarms.]

Usually the exterior has checkering or stippling molded into it for an even more secure hold.

Pachmayr is the best known of the aftermarket rubberized grip manufacturers; it offers rubberized "Signature" grips for the SIG-Sauer P226 with a price tag of $30.50 per set. Uncle Mike's also offers replacement pairs of rubberized grips for the P226; cost is $18.95.

Hogue offers both rubber and wooden grips for several of the SIG-Sauer guns. The company's soft rubberized grips are available for the P220 "American" P226, P228, and P229; retail price is $21 each. Hogue also offers a "Handall" soft rubber sleeve that will fit most medium sized guns including all the SIG-Sauer guns as well as the P210 and P240; this sleeve slips

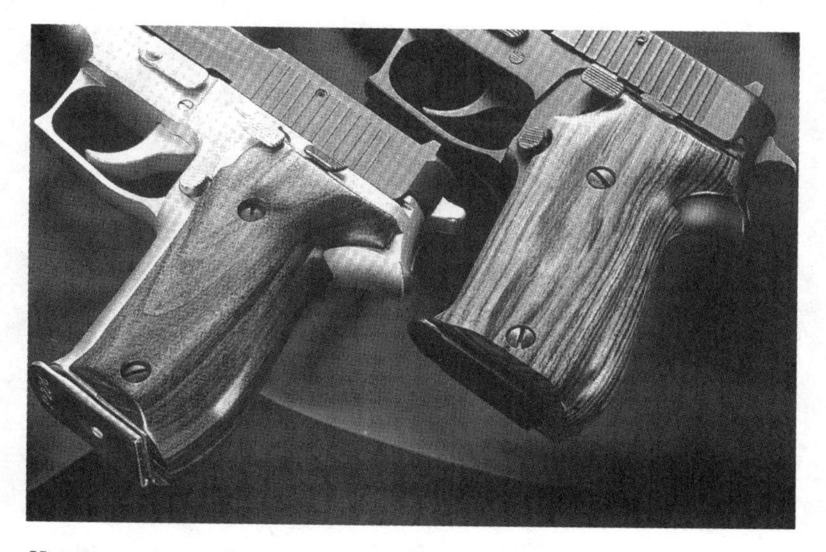

Hogue exotic wood grips shown here on two SIG-Sauer pistols. [Photo courtesy of Hogue.]

over the original grip of the pistol. On the downside, it adds girth to the pistol and therefore isn't ideal for those with small hands. But many shooters with larger hands love it because of its finger grooves which wrap around the front of the pistol frame, creating a very secure hold that brings the gun back on target rapidly. The cost is only $10.

For the SIG-Sauer P230, Hogue also offers the "Handall, Jr." which is similar to the Handall, but scaled down for smaller pistols and has only one finger swell molded into its surface. Cost is only $10.

Hogue's wooden grips are available in a variety of fancy and exotic hardwoods including goncalo alves, pau ferro, lamo camo (giving a laminated camouflage pattern), kingwood, tulipwood, coco bolo, and rosewood; these are available for the P220 "American", P220 European, P226, P228, and P229. Cost runs from $30 to $60, depending on the type of wood the buyer desires. These grips are offered with smooth finishes; checkered finishes are available for a slight additional cost. For the best in feel and looks Hogue grips can't be beat.

Hogue rubberized grips shown here on two SIG-Sauer pistols. [Photo courtesy of Hogue.]

Recently a new "customized" grip has become available in the form of "Mastergrip." This product is built around a plastic that hardens in ultraviolet light (in most cases, sunlight). The gun owner wraps the flexible plastic around the front or side of the pistol's grip plates, then grasps it tightly to make the soft material conform to his fingers. The plastic oozes around the shooter's digits, creating a mold that is personalized right down to the fingerprints. The plastic is then placed in the sunlight so it can cure. Once hardened, the plastic mold is placed on the pistol grip and a black rubberized sleeve slipped over the grip. The sleeve "shrinks" down to the contours of the grip and plastic insert, creating a smooth and professional-looking grip surface that is now customized to the shooter's hand. Both the sleeve and insert are impervious to cleaning fluids and oils.

Mastergrip, like the slip-over Handall, adds girth to a grip making it less than ideal for shooters with small hands. But for many shooters, this may be just the ticket for a gun that truly fits the hand.

Handi-Hider

The Choate Machine & Tool "Handi-Hider" is a small metal bar welded to a plate with four screw holes in it. This plate can be attached to walls, under a table, or a variety of other places permitting sliding a pistol onto it, with the vinyl-coated rod slipping into the barrel. This enables a gun owner to hide a SIG or SIG-Sauer pistol in a variety of out-of-sight places while still having the pistol close by, ready to be grabbed and brought into play at a moment's notice.

While care has to be taken not to hide the gun where a child might discover it, this system is ideal for many businessmen who want to have a gun handy in case of a holdup, while not frightening gun-shy customers. And homeowners often discover that the Handi-Hider is perfect for keeping a gun close to the bed, ready to deal with a burglar. The Handi-Holder costs $7.50 with models available with 90 or 45 degree post angles and rod diameters of 9mm (which also accommodates the .380) or .45 available.

Holsters

Untold pistols are carried worldwide in the so-called "Mexican Holster" (i.e., carrying a pistol inside the waistband of the shooter's pants). Cheap, this "holster" works—most of the time. But it isn't comfortable for any length of time and the firearm is always in danger of dropping out at an inopportune time or apt to slide into the pants and down a leg with embarrassing, if not disastrous results. Little wonder most "pros" use a real holster.

For collectors of SIG P210 pistols, it's possible to purchase the leather military holster used by Swiss officers. This flapped holster has a magazine pouch sewn to its forward edge and is sold by Mandall's Shooting Supplies. However, its $250 price tag makes it appealing only to collectors.

Excellent leather holsters are available for any of the guns covered in this manual, but leather holsters are generally expensive and don't protect a firearm as well as nylon and Cordura holsters do. Consequently a shooter is well advised to first try out a holster made of these synthetic materials since they're tough and don't promote corrosion—and are inexpensive to buy.

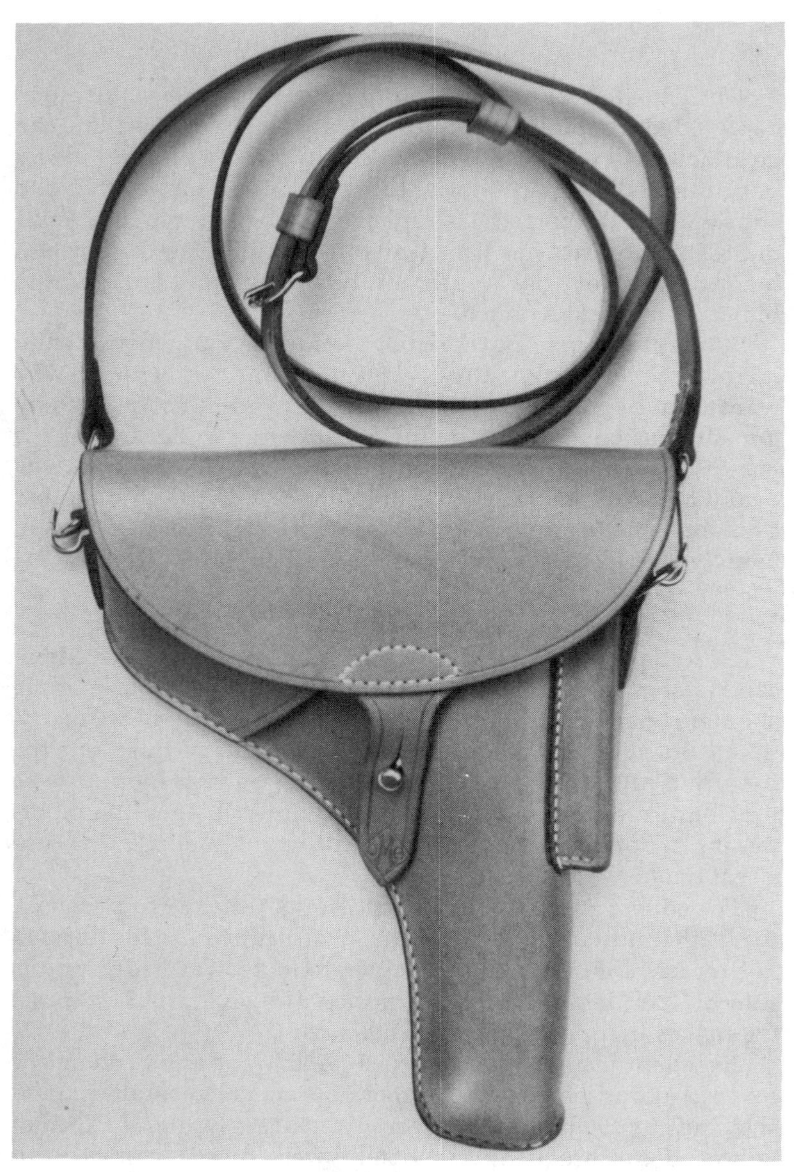

SIG P210 pistol holster.
[Photo courtesy of Mandall's Shooting Supplies, Inc.]

That's not to say there aren't some quality leather holsters available. DeSantis, Milt Sparks, Alessi, and Triple K all offer excellent, albeit expensive, leather rigs that are hard to beat and which are molded to fit guns exactly.

For those with less cash to spend, Brigade Quartermaster markets a number of nylon holsters and accessories designed for military, police, and civilian users. The company's "Quickfire" consists of a nylon holster that can be adjusted for large and small pistols thanks to a Velcro strap and an open base. The Quickfire uses a thumb break strap so a pistol carried in it is very secure; cost is $15. Police or other shooters interested in the low-slung SAS-type holster will find Brigade Quartermasters' "Hi-Tac Assault Holster" to their liking. The flapped holster comes with all the straps needed to sling it from a belt and a secondary strap to secure it to the shooter's thigh. Fastex buckles and Velcro allow easy mounting and adjustment of the holster and a magazine pouch along its front edge makes it easy to carry spare ammunition. The black nylon pouch is padded and waterproofed; the price is $50.

Another of Brigade Quartermasters' holsters, is the "Archangel" which is similar to the Hi-Tac but lacks the front magazine pouch and flap and costs $40. For those selecting the SAS MK IV or the Hi-Tac, the company also offers the "SAS Flash-Bang Belt/Leg Pouch" which can be worn on the off-hand side, hanging from the belt and strapped to the leg to accommodate three fragmentation or smoke grenades; cost is $45.

The best bargain in the holster arena is from Michaels of Oregon in the form of their "Uncle Mike's" police and civilian holsters. Constructed of tough Cordura, these holsters are readily available at many gun stores. The Uncle Mike's belt holsters will fit onto most belts or can be worn on the company's inexpensive "Sidekick Holster Belts" designed for them. These belts have a quick release buckle making it easy to adjust and put on; they're available in brown, black, and camo. Cost is $8 apiece.

Uncle Mike's "Sidekick" holster has an adjustable snap strap to secure the gun. Sandwiched between the inner and outer skin of the holster is a thick, waterproof foam padding that makes the holster conform to the gun carried in it for a "custom fit." Available in black or camo finishes, the price for the Sidekick is $15.

For police and security guards, Uncle Mike's "Duty Holster" with thumb-break snap is ideal; cost is $30. Uncle Mike's "Duty System" series of pouches and accessories is also offered for policemen; various pouches in this series are designed to hold magazines, radios, mace, batons, flashlights, handcuffs, and keys.

Uncle Mike's reversible (left or right hand) horizontal shoulder harness holster is ideal for concealed carry under a jacket. The "Horizontal Shoulder" with two straps crossing in the back, or the "Undercover Horizontal" using the more conventional method of looping the off-hand strap over the shoulder and back across the lower back (for superior concealment) are both ideal. Cost for the Horizontal Shoulder holster is $30 while the Undercover Horizontal retails at $25.

Concealing a pistol on a belt is considerably more comfortable than shoulder harness systems. Uncle Mike's black "Super Belt Slide" pancake holster is ideal for such carry and is offered for $18. The company also sells an ultra-thin "Inside-the-Pant" holster which clips to the belt. Uncle Mike's "Ankle Holster", selling for $27, will accommodate the P230, though many shooters may not like having this much weight on their ankle and should experiment a bit before adopting it for full-time use.

In addition to holsters, Uncle Mike's single and double magazine pouches, fanny packs, and other pouches designed for hunting and outdoor use, all designed to match the finish of the company's Sidekick holsters and belts.

Shooters who add a laser sight or flashlight under the barrel of their SIG-Sauer need a special holster designed to accommodate the larger bulk of the entire assembly. Fortunately two such holsters are available. TacStar Industries distributes a "Universal Pistol Laser Holster" for laser sighted SIG-Sauers. Constructed of black ballistic nylon, the "PLH-R" is the right-hand model while the "PLH-L" is the left-hand model. Both have thumb-break straps and cost $30 each. Uncle Mike's product line includes a holster designed to accommodate an under-the-barrel laser; available in black, it has a thumb-break safety similar to that of the company's duty holster. Cost is $30.

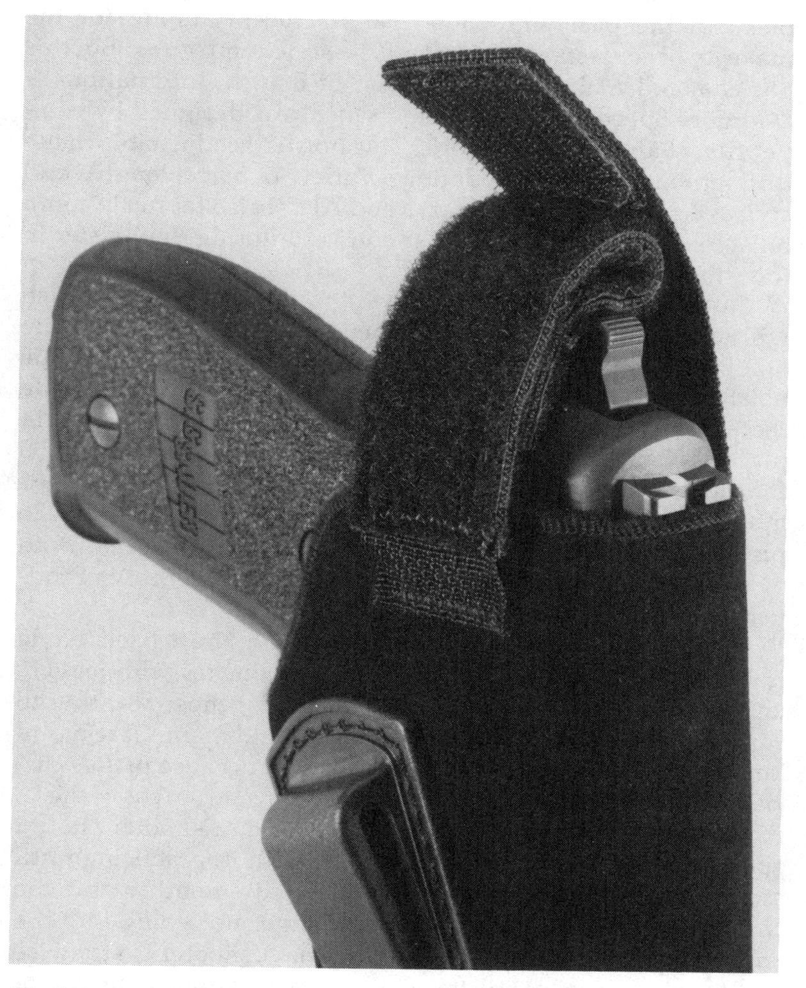

Uncle Mike's "Inside-the-Pant" holster has a Velcro thumb strap. [Photo courtesy of Michaels of Oregon.]

For those needing a competition holster, things have been bleak in the past with most manufacturers aiming for the majority of contestants shooting 1911-style comp guns. But this has changed with the introduction of Bianchi International's "Gilmore Speed Leader" holster which was designed by competition champ Riley Gilmore. This holster is adjustable in ten different areas, accommodating a variety of barrel lengths and styles of guns. And Milt Sparks and Alessi also fabricate comp holsters designed for contest shooting, tailoring the holster to the shooter's firearm.

Safariland has also created several "Paddle Holsters" which will accommodate scoped SIG-Sauer's. These holsters are made of a laminate plastic which locks itself around the pistol. The holster itself is designed to be worn with its inner section inside the waistband, doing away with the need for a belt to hold it in place. A Belt Loop Accessory can be purchased for it for $8.50 for those wishing for a more traditional carry. The 5181-77-61 model of the Safariland Paddle Holster fits the P220 and P226 pistols. The 5181-79-61 fits the SIG-Sauer P225 and P228. Both of these Safariland holsters are available from Ed Brown Products and the cost is $47 per holster.

Several companies have come out with "butt pack" style holsters. Given the popularity of these pouches with joggers and tourists, this makes an ideal holster for those wanting to carry a pistol without alarming those around them. Care has to be exercised with these holsters, however, because pistols carried in them are considered "concealed" in many areas of the U. S.. Regardless of the style of holster used, a shooter should spend a lot of time becoming familiar with it, practicing until snaps or other fasteners can be operated smoothly and the firearm presented quickly (with the finger not going into the trigger guard until the gun is on target). A shooter is also wise to always wear pistol holsters in the same location on the belt or under the shoulder. Switching holster positions from shoulder carry to side carry, for example, can cause a shooter to "go for his gun" in an emergency, only to discover that it's elsewhere. Such a mistake can be fatal.

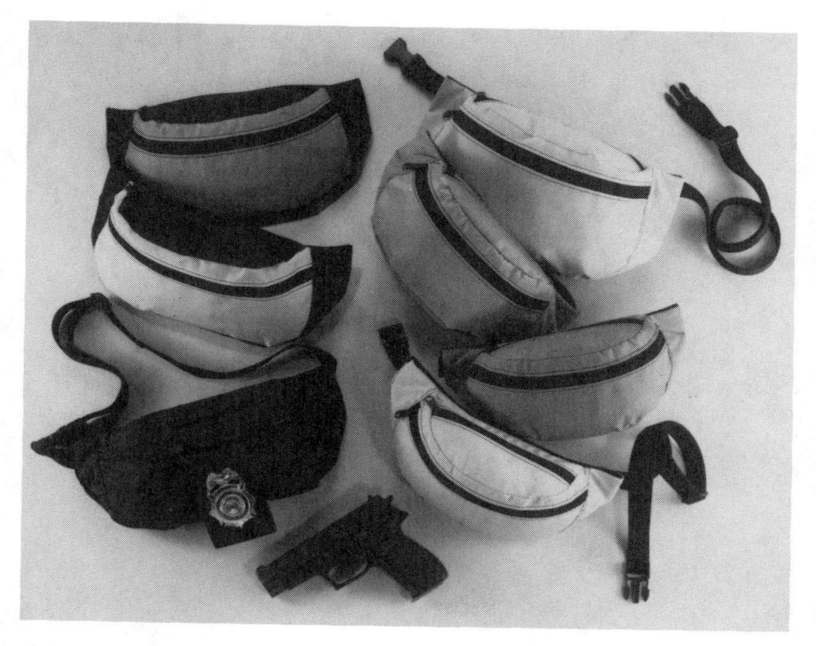

Uncle Mike's "GunRunner Fanny Pack" style holster can conceal large pistols. [Photo courtesy of Michaels of Oregon.]

Magazines

The magazine is the most significant part of a semiauto pistol in terms of reliability; damaged magazines cause most pistol malfunctions. The SIG and its spinoffs all have magazines which are very well designed and function flawlessly when properly cared for; but they can be easily damaged. This makes the first line of pistol maintenance proper care and protection of magazines. Shooters should avoid denting magazines, should never do anything which might bend the feed lips of a magazine, and must keep the magazine clean. A damaged magazine creates an unreliable pistol.

Shooters needing new magazines should first consider purchasing them directly from the importer of their firearm. Magazines are manufactured to the close tolerances and SIG and SIG-Sauer take pains to make their magazines perfect.

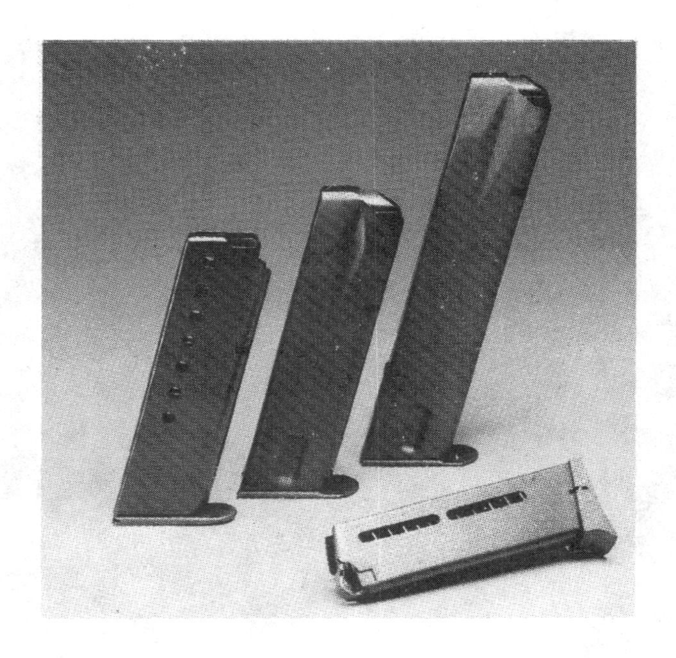

SIG-Sauer magazines are the best bet for the company's pistols since they are made to exacting standards. [Photo courtesy of Sigarms.]

Unfortunately, the Clinton Administration's 1994 Crime Bill took the misguided action of suspending the manufacture of magazines with capacities over 10 rounds, thereby assuring that only criminals would have access to new magazines after this cutoff date. This law is arguably a farce, given the fact that most shootings involving criminal attacks are over with just one or two shots (while those forced to defend themselves against a gang of criminals might need more than ten shots). But the law is the law, ass or not. And this law will make it harder and more expensive for honest folks to get replacement magazines for the SIG-Sauer or other high-capacity firearms.

There is some good news. The law doesn't apply to magazines manufactured before the bill was signed into law. And Clinton lobbied Congressmen telling them they had to pass the measure before the August recess because "criminals don't go on vacation." Congress passed the law and Clinton (perhaps disproving his contention that criminals don't do so) went on vacation—before signing the bill.

This gave magazine manufacturers a window of opportunity to continue to make high-capacity magazines that would soon become worth much more than before as shooters made sure they had enough spare magazines on hand to supply their pistols. The manufacturers worked feverishly, creating huge stocks of magazines that will only increase in value during the next few years as the supplies slowly dwindle.

Fortunately magazines that are properly cared for last almost forever. And if stored loaded for long periods of time, quality magazine springs won't get a set that keeps them from feeding ammunition reliably. Such a happenstance is rare and generally occurs only with cheap magazines or those created when a country is at war and the spring hasn't been properly heat treated. Consequently it's unnecessary to purchase spare magazines so ammunition can be "rotated" from one magazine to another to allow the springs in the magazines to rest. Modern magazine springs don't "set" any more than the recoil or hammer spring in the pistol does.

Shooters using a pistol for comp shooting or who practice quick reloads, dropping a magazine out of the pistol and rapidly inserting a full one, may wish to add a bumper pad to the base of their magazines to help reduce damage done to the magazines. This protects the magazine somewhat, makes it a bit easier to seat the magazine when reloading, and also offers support to the pinky finger for shooters with large hands.

SIG-Sauer manufactures harder rubber floor plates for P220 and P226 pistols. These are ideal for use on these guns and fit perfectly, simply replacing the floor plate on the magazine and making it possible to easily replace the original plate if the shooter so desires.

Pachmayr magazine pads are currently offered by Brownells in sets of 5 with the MBK-39 fitting the single-column 9mm magazines and the MBK-59 ideal for double-column 9mm, .40, and .357 SIG magazines; cost is $15 per set of five. Contact cement is the easiest and best way to attach bumper pads to the floor plate of a magazine.

Contest shooters sometimes add a brass or aluminum bumper pad to magazines to increase the weight of the slide, making it slip out of the pistol quickly when it's released and making it more apt to land on the base rather than the easily-bent lips. Currently these metal bumper pads have to be handmade for the SIG-Sauer pistols. Provided the shooter can locate the materials (often available at a nearby metal working shop), this isn't beyond a do-it-yourselfer's skills, provided a little care is taken to proceed slowly and keep the file work flat and squared rather than rounding surfaces. Epoxy cement is most ideal for attaching these pads to the magazine base plate.

Shooters wanting a higher capacity magazine for their automatics may have their work cut out for them, given the manufacturing ban currently in effect in the U. S.. Provided the magazine can be found, upgrading to a 20-round capacity is a simple proposition for the P226 and P228 since they'll accept the higher capacity magazine SIG-Sauer designed for them.

Ram-Line also offers several higher capacity magazines that have a compact size, thanks to a flat coiled spring (similar to those in old-style mechanical clocks) which the company uses

Ram-Line high-capacity magazine. [Photo courtesy of Ram-Line.]

in its magazines rather than the spiral spring found in most other companies' magazines. The coiled spring is fastened to the top of the magazine's wall and to the bottom of the magazine follower, leaving the area under the follower empty and increasing the magazine capacity by several cartridges or more.

An additional benefit of Ram-Line's spring is that its tension doesn't increase as rapidly as it does in older-style magazines. This creates a constant tension arrangement where the last few cartridges inserted into the magazine (or the first extracted) don't need more pressure than the first ones put into it. Needless to say, this makes reloading a magazine less of a chore and improves the functioning of many guns.

The one shortcoming with Ram-Line's system is the permanently mounted spring which is attached to the follower so they can't be disassembled for cleaning. But cleaning isn't hard to carry out since the floor plate can easily be slipped off giving access to almost the entire inside of the magazine (and, in fact, the magazine will actually function without the base plate in place). Ram-Line's current offering of constant tension, spiral-spring magazines contains an 18-round magazine for the P226 and a 15-rounder for the P228. Thanks to the Ram-Line design, neither magazine extends any farther from the magazine well of the pistol than does the standard SIG-Sauer magazine.

Magazine Loading Tools

Contest shooters or others who regularly spend a lot of time at the range often suffer sore fingers after cramming cartridges into seemingly endless magazines. For those who need to load magazines, help has come in the form of loading tools that chuck cartridges into magazines more rapidly and effortlessly than can be done by hand.

HKS Products, Inc., offers the "Speed Loader", a levered tool that fits onto a magazine where thumb action shoves a cartridge down into a double-column 9mm or .40 SIG-Sauer magazine to allow another round to be inserted easily. The lever gives the user an added mechanical advantage and makes it possible to insert cartridges into a magazine at the rate of one per second. Cost is $10.

Ram-Line's "X-Press Loader" is a bit faster (though it takes longer to set up). This system handles double-column 9mm magazines. To use it, the shooter first places a magazine into the assembly and adjusts the bar to hold it in place. Then cartridges are dropped into the ammo hopper and a lever pulled, activating an arm that shoves the cartridge into the magazine. The X-Press Loader costs $29.97. Ram-Line also sells a "Pick Up Tube" which allows cartridges to be quickly picked up from a table top or other flat surface, aligning them so they can be dropped into an X-Press Loader; cost is $10.97.

Magazine Pouches

Because the magazine is critical to the proper functioning of any of the pistols in this manual, it's important to carry magazines in a pouch or other container that protects them. A bump or drop on the lip of a magazine can quickly turn it into a piece of junk and some lint picked up in a pocket can cause a jam when it and a cartridge try to share space in the chamber of a barrel. The best protection for a spare magazine is to carry it in a quality magazine pouch.

In general, military magazine pouches designed for the Beretta M9 (92F) or Browning Hi-Power will fit the double-column 9mm magazines listed in this book. But fit gets a little iffy sometimes and requires some experimentation. Nevertheless, it's possible to find "army surplus" pouches to accommodate most of the magazines for the various SIG and SIG-Sauer pistols.

A better bet is Uncle Mike's double magazine pouches. These are ideal for carrying magazines and come in two models, one which will fit the single column SIG-Sauer 9mm magazines and another which will accommodate double-column 9mm, .40, and .357 SIG magazines as well as .45 magazines. The pouches are available in both camouflage and black and fit perfectly on the company's belts; price is $14 per pouch.

Contest shooters, especially those using the Safariland paddle holsters, should consider the Safariland "Paddle Magazine Holder" since it matches the holster and also doesn't require a belt to hold it in place, making it very quick to put on or take off.

Each holder is constructed from a molded polymer that holds a magazine securely while still allowing it to be pulled from the top of the holder without unfastening any flaps, snaps, or Velcro tabs. This makes it ideal for competition, though not so suitable for self-defense purposes. The Paddle Magazine Holder (catalog number 074-76-6) fits all the SIG-Sauer magazines.

Replacement Spring Kits

Gunsmiths and contest shooters, as well as more than a few "kitchen table gunsmiths" have, over the years, modified pistols by changing the springs in them. Sometimes this can have admirable results; many times the end result is an unreliable or even dangerous combination of parts. Shooters who are interested in reliability and who will be firing full-power loads are well advised to leave things alone on their pistols since SIG and SIG-Sauer engineers have spent a lot of time and money tuning and optimizing their handguns and those who think they're going to discover a better way of doing things with these guns are undoubtedly headed for grave disappointment.

On the other hand, contest shooters who are using less powerful rounds may discover that lighter recoil springs make their pistol function more reliably. And some "comp" shooters may wish to lower the double-action pull on double/single-action guns by replacing hammer or trigger springs. But the end result of such modifications is a gun that should *only* be used for contests since full power loads may damage it and it is apt to malfunction from time to time to boot, especially if not kept meticulously clean. Malfunctions on the playing field may cost dollars or a contest; in real life confrontations they can cost the shooter his life.

Another time a shooter might consider replacing the springs in his pistol is after it has been fired extensively or the springs modified by a previous owner. In such cases, replacing the springs can revamp a tired pistol back to its original configuration and turn an abused pistol into a reliable gun again.

Brownells offers several "Pro-Spring" kits designed to modify a pistol for special ammunition or revamp it back to its original spring configuration. These kits have standard recoil, firing pin, and hammer springs plus a lighter recoil spring for use with reduced loads. Great care should be exercised with the lighter spring since firing full-power loads with a light spring can damage a pistol's slide or frame.

Brownells' Pro-Spring "SSP-700" kit is designed for the P220; the "SSP-701" kit is for the P226. Cost of each kit is $13.

*****

The SIG, SIG-Sauer, and SIG-Hammerli pistols, especially with the newest versions of these guns, are perfect for most shooters right out of the box. But for a few individuals, the right accessories and modifications can improve the gun for their specialized needs. The shooter must select only the accessories he needs, and then practice carefully to master his shooting skills. Good shooters don't get that way because of the accessories they own or the modifications they've made to their pistols. Good shooters get to their skill level through careful and time-consuming practice. There isn't any shortcut.

Although they're all precise machines that can spit out bullets for hours on end without a hiccup, like any other machines the pistols covered in this book must be cared for properly if they're not to suffer reliability problems or be ruined.

Of prime consideration is proper lubrication between the various moving parts of the firearm. This is especially critical with the stainless steel slide SIG-Sauer guns. Occasionally owners of stainless steel and alloy frame firearms assume that lubrication isn't necessary since rust isn't much of a problem. In such a case, the guns will quickly start to bind when fired with cartridges failing to extract or chamber. (Shooters can use minimal amounts of lubricant on pistols having electroless nickel finishes and sometimes get away with it due to the natural lubricating qualities of this finish. But even here such a practice is asking for trouble.)

Oils designed for electrical engines or penetrating oils like WD40 are best avoided on firearms for two reasons. First these lubricants often solidify over time when exposed to the air; this creates binding problems that cause a firearm to malfunction. Second, penetrating oil is more apt than regular gun oils to deactivate the cartridge in a firearm—not a pretty picture in a defense arm or one being used for a high-stake contest.

The best bet is to purchase one of the all-purpose cleaning/

lubricating solvents designed for firearms; Tri-Lube, Break-Free CLP, or one of the other formulas is perfect. The shooter should then be sure to oil all moving parts and exterior blued steel surfaces, taking care not to get any lubricant on cartridges or leave excessive amounts where it might run onto cartridges. The only time excessive oil should be left on a firearm is when it's to be stored for a long period of time.

Excessive lubricant also acts like a dust magnet, collecting grit that can become like tiny files on moving surfaces. Excessive oil can also damage wooden grips, soil holsters, and even stain clothing. Too much of a good thing is always bad and oil on firearms is no exception.

Cleaning a gun dictates its disassembly if the job is to be done properly (more on disassembly steps in a moment). A pistol should never be cleaned from the muzzle end of things since this can damage the lands at the end of the barrel, ruining accuracy. Instead brushes and swabs should travel from the chamber toward the muzzle and then on out, not returning since that drags fouling back into the bore, defeating much of the work that's being done.

As for the cleaning kit, a visit to a gunstore will turn up a variety of cleaning kits complete with brushes sized to fit the 9mm/.357-, .40-, or .45-sized bore. For those who are "into" SIG-Sauer products, it's even possible to purchase the company's cleaning kit designed for use with the SIG-Sauer pistols.

If time isn't a concern, the first thing to do is send a swab or the bore brush through the barrel after soaking the instrument to the point of dripping with liberal amounts of solvent. Then the barrel should be set aside for a half hour so the solvent can really break down the dirt in the barrel.

A cleaning brush soaked in solvent is then shoved down the bore to break up the last of the fouling deposits coating the inside of the barrel. If this chore is done regularly, then buildup from metal jackets will be easily removed, saving a lot of work in the long run and also avoiding the possibility of dangerous chamber pressures produced when the bore is "contracted" in size by excessive metal buildup inside it.

Once the major grime is broken up by the brush, cloth or

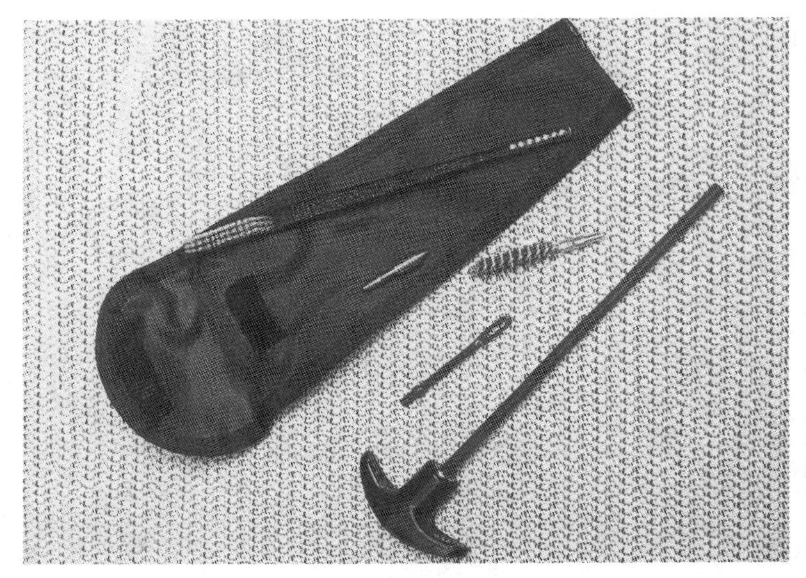

SIG-Sauer cleaning kit. [Photo courtesy of Sigarms.]

paper towel swabs are sent through the bore, again moving from the chamber to the muzzle. Some shooters prefer jags for this chore while others like the slotted cleaning tools popular in the U. S. Either will do the job just fine.

SOP entails sending a dry patch through the bore followed by a patch soaked in solvent. This alternating process continues until the patches start to come through clean. If the gun is to be stored away, the operation ends with an oil-soaked patch going though the bore. If the gun is to be loaded, a dry patch is sent through last to keep the oil from ruining the accuracy of the first shot as well as to prevent the deactivation of the cartridge by the lubricant.

For long-term storage of a pistol, Outers "Metal Seal" or another lubricant designed to help prevent rust is a good idea. This product is available at most large gun stores and has recently enjoyed great popularity as many Americans who distrust their government stock up on supplies that will enable them to bury their firearms rather than have them confiscated.

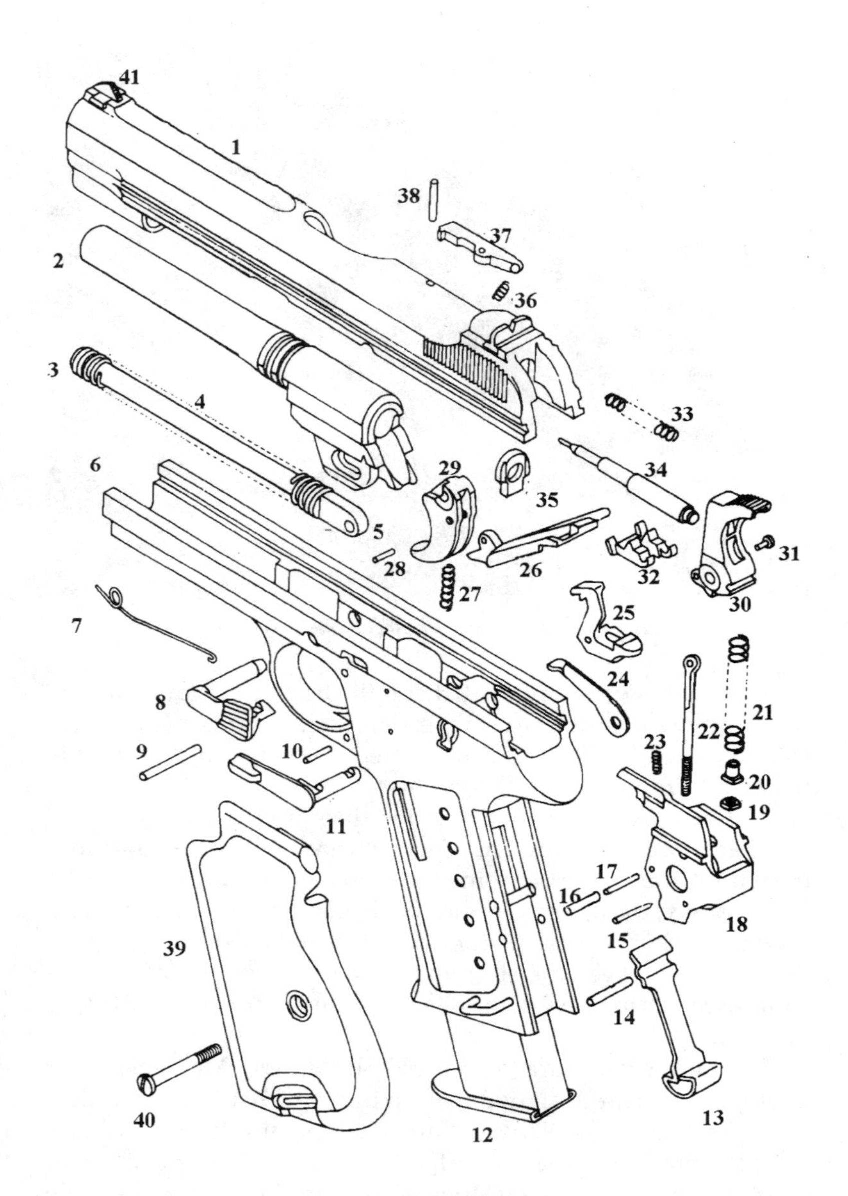

Exploded drawing of P210 pistol.

Parts numbers for P210 illustration

1. Slide
2. Barrel
3. Recoil spring
4. Recoil spring guide
5. Recoil spring guide tip
6. Frame
7. Slide catch spring
8. Slide catch
9. Trigger pin
10. Retaining pin
11. Safety lever
12. Magazine
13. Magazine catch
14. Magazine catch pin
15. Hammer assembly pin
16. Hammer assembly pin
17. Hammer assembly pin
18. Hammer assembly housing
19. Hammer strut nut
20. Hammer strut pressure plate
21. Hammer strut spring
22. Hammer strut
23. Spring
24. Magazine disconnect safety
25. Lower half of sear assembly
26. Trigger bar
27. Trigger spring
28. Trigger pin
29. Trigger
30. Hammer
31. Hammer strut pin
32. Upper half of sear assembly
33. Firing pin spring
34. Firing pin
35. Firing pin retaining plate
36. Extractor spring
37. Extractor
38. Extractor pin
39. Left grip plate (right plate not shown)
40. Grip plate screw (right grip plate screw not shown)
41. Front sight

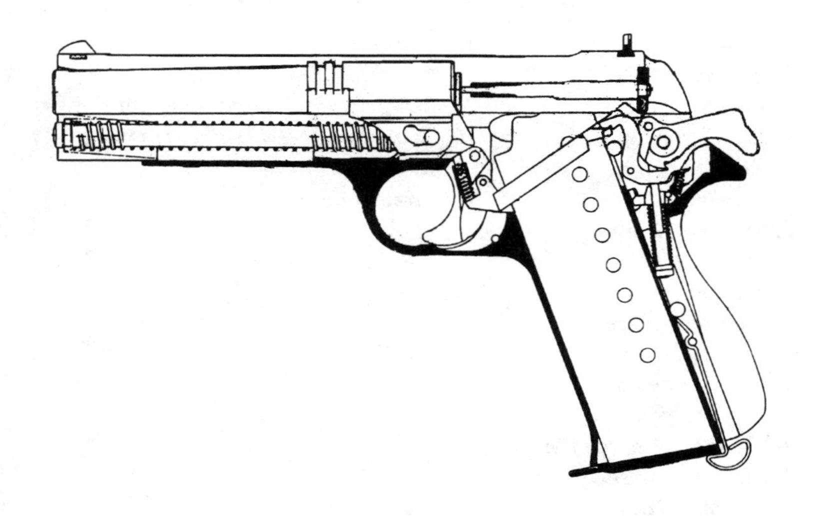

Cutaway drawing of P210 pistol.

The following sections give the steps for field stripping the various SIG and SIG-Sauer pistols for cleaning.

Field Stripping the SIG Model 49/P210

Except for the removable hammer assembly, field stripping the SIG pistols is much like field stripping a Browning High Power M35 automatic. The operation isn't all that complicated once you get the hang of it. Here's the procedure:

1) The magazine should first be removed and the firearm cycled to be sure it's empty.

2) The slide is drawn back a half inch so the disassembly notch on the slide lines up with the rear of the slide stop. At this point the slide stop is pushed out from left to right.

3) The slide is eased forward along its tracks until it is off the frame.

4) The slide assembly is turned upside down and the spring guide carefully eased forward and lifted out, taking care

to retain it since it's under spring pressure. The spring on most guides is "captive" and should be left on the spring guide.

5) The barrel can now be lifted out of the slide.

6) The hammer assembly can be lifted up and out of the frame with a little wiggling. The unit that comes free will include the hammer, disconnector, sear, hammer spring, and the hammer spring guide rod. Generally it is best to leave these assembled.

7) The firing pin can be removed by pushing its rear end forward to clear its plate and then lifting the plate upward out of the slide. Care should be taken to retain the firing pin since it is under spring pressure.

This gives the shooter access to all the parts that need to be cleaned. Further disassembly is not recommended. Reassembly is basically a reverse of this process.

Field Stripping the SIG-Sauer P220-229

Field stripping a P220 series of pistols is simple, thanks to a convenient takedown lever. To field strip one of these pistols:

1) The magazine should first be removed and the firearm cycled to be sure it is empty.

2) Using the slide catch (just above the left grip panel), manually lock the slide open.

3) Locate the release lever on the left side of the frame, just above and slightly to the rear of the front of the trigger guard and rotate it downward a quarter turn.

4) Grasp the slide, depress the slide release, and ease the slide forward along its tracks until it is off the frame.

6) The slide assembly is turned upside down and the spring and its guide carefully eased forward and lifted out, taking care to retain both since they're under spring pressure.

5) The barrel can now be lifted out of the slide.

This gives the shooter access to all the parts that need to be cleaned. Further disassembly is not recommended. Reassembly is basically a reverse of this process.

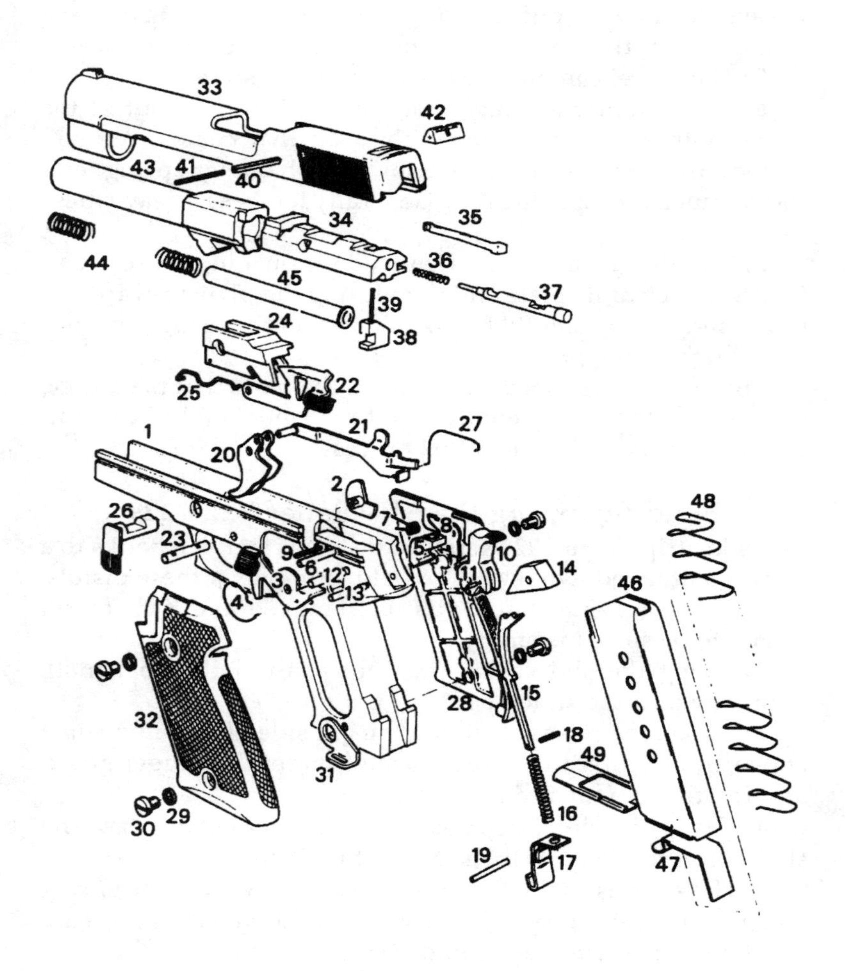

Exploded drawing of SIG-Sauer P220

Parts numbers for P220 illustration

1. Frame
2. Decocking lever seating
3. Decocking lever
4. Decocking lever spring
5. Sear
6. Sear pin
7. Torsion spring for sear
8. Safety lever
9. Spring pin
10. Hammer
11. Hammer pin
12. Hammer pivot pin
13. Pin for stop
14. Stop
15. Hammer spring stirrup
16. Hammer spring
17. Magazine catch
18. Hammer spring pin
19. Magazine catch pin
20. Trigger
21. Trigger rod
22. Slide catch\release lever
23. Trigger pin
24. Locking insert
25. Slide catch spring
26. Takedown lever
27. Trigger spring
28. Right grip plate
29. Grip screw washer
30. Grip screw
31. Lanyard ring
32. Left grip plate
33. Slide
34. Rear insert
35. Extractor
36. Firing pin spring
37. Firing pin
38. Internal safety
39. Safety spring
40. Outer spring pin
41. Inner spring pin
42. Rear sight
43. Barrel
44. Recoil spring
45. Recoil spring guide
46. Magazine body
47. Magazine follower
48. Magazine spring
49. Magazine base plate

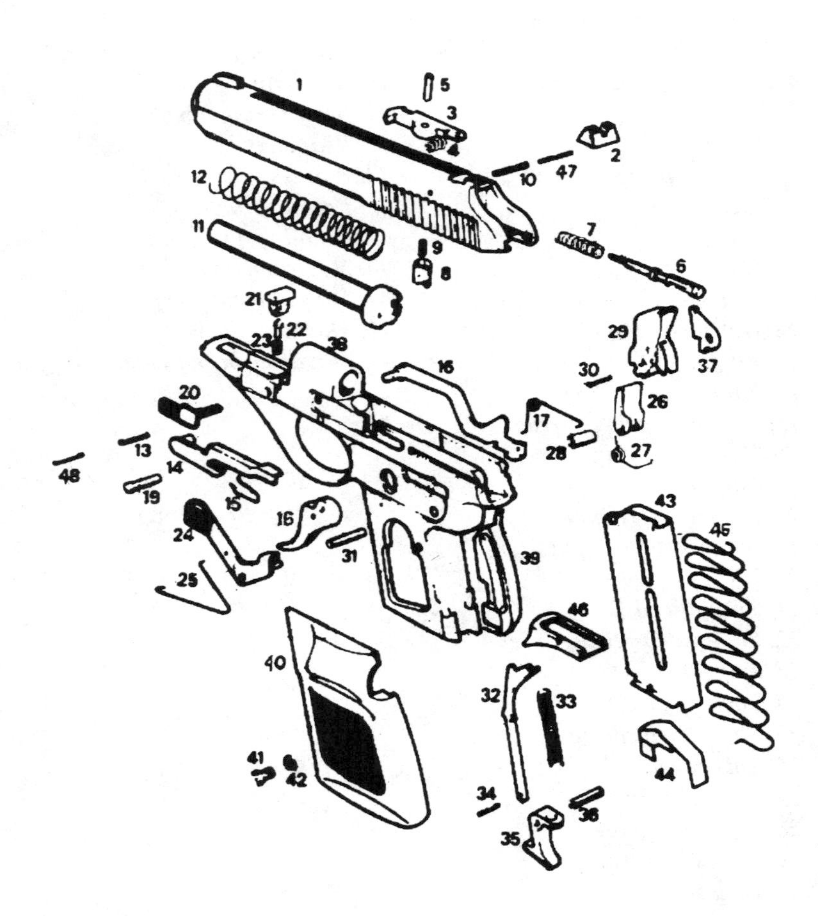

Exploded drawing of SIG-Sauer P230

Parts numbers for P230 illustration

1. Slide
2. Rear sight
3. Extractor
4. Extractor spring
5. Extractor pin
6. Firing pin
7. Firing pin spring
8. Automatic safety
9. Safety spring
10. Outer spring pin
11. Barrel
12. Recoil Spring
13. Barrel cross pin
14. Slide stop
15. Slide stop spring
16. Trigger rod
17. Trigger rod spring
18. Trigger
19. Trigger pin
20. Takedown lever
21. Takedown lever captive
22. Takedown lever captive detent
23. Takedown lever captive detent spring
24. Hammer drop lever
25. Hammer drop lever spring
26. Sear
27. Sear spring
28. Sear pivot pin
29. Hammer
30. Hammer pin
31. Hammer drop lever pin
32. Hammer spring stirrup
33. Hammer spring
34. Hammer spring stirrup pin
35. Magazine catch
36. Magazine catch pin
37. Automatic safety lever
38. Frame
39. Right grip plate (partial)
40. Left grip plate
41. Left grip plate screw (right grip plate screw not shown)
42. Left grip plate screw washer (right grip plate screw washer not shown)
43. Magazine
44. Magazine follower
45. Magazine spring
46. Magazine floor plate
47. Inner spring pin
48. Barrel cross pin

Field Stripping the SIG-Sauer P230

Field stripping a P230 pistol is slightly different from the other SIG-Sauer guns due to its fixed barrel and blow-back design. To field strip the P230:

1) The magazine should first be removed and the firearm cycled to be sure it is empty.

2) Locate the release lever on the left side of the frame, just above and slightly to the rear of the front of the trigger guard and rotate it downward a quarter turn.

3) Ease the slide backward and lift it at its rear. This will release it from its tracks on the frame. Now ease the slide forward and off the barrel.

4) The recoil spring can now be eased forward off the barrel.

This gives the shooter access to all the parts that need to be cleaned. Further disassembly is not recommended. Reassembly is basically a reversal of this process.

Disassembly of Magazines

Most magazines for the above firearms can be disassembled by shoving the base plate forward and off the magazine. This frees the spring and magazine follower which must be restrained since the spring is under pressure. Great care is necessary to keep track of the follower and its spring since each part has a top, bottom, forward, and rear sides; inserting the follower or spring into the magazine incorrectly during reassembly will lead to malfunctions.

A very light coating of oil will aid in magazine functioning and prevent rust on blued steel surfaces. Excess oil must be wiped away if the magazine is to be used in the near future as lubricant can deactivate ammunition.

Appendix A
Suppliers of Accessories and Firearms

Aimpoint, USA 580 Herndon Parkway, Suite 500 Herndon, VA 22070	703-471-6828
Applied Laser Systems 2160 N. W. Vine St., Unit A Grant's Pass, OR 97526	503-474-6560
B-Square Company Box 11281 Ft. Worth, TX 76110	800-433-2909
Bausch & Lomb/Bushnell 9200 Cody Overland Park, KS 66214	800-423-3537
Bianchi International, Inc. 100 Calle Cortez Temecula, CA 92590	714-676-5621
Brigade Quartermasters 8025 Cobb International Blvd. Kennesaw, GA 30144-4349	404-428-1248

Brownells, Inc. Rt. 2, Box 1 Montezuma, IA 50171	515-623-5401
Choate Machine & Tool Box 218 Bald Knob, AR 72010-0218	501-724-6193
Delta Force P.O. Box 1625 El Dorado, AR 71731-1625	800-852-4445
Ed Brown Products Rt. 2, Box 2922 Perry, MO 63462	314-565-3261
Emerging Technologies, Inc. P. O. Box 3548 Little Rock, AR 72203	501-375-2227
Hesco, Inc. 2821 Greenville Rd. LaGrange, GA 30240	404-884-7967
Hogue Grips P.O. Box 2038 Apascadero, CA 93423	800-438-4747
Laser Devices 2 Harris Court, A4 Monterey, CA 93940	800-235-2162
Laser Products 18300 Mt. Baldy Circle Fountain Valley, CA 92708-6117	714-545-9444
Mag-na-port International 41302 Executive Dr. Mt. Clemens, MI 48045-3448	313-469-6727

Mandall Shooting Supplies
3616 N. Scottsdale Rd.
Scottsdale, AZ 85252 602-945-2553

Mastergrip/Keeco Impressions, Inc.
P.O. Box 950033
Lake Mary, FL 32795 407-321-4005

Michaels of Oregon Company
P. O. Box 13010
Portland, OR 97213 503-255-6890

Wayne Novak's .45 Shop
P. O. Box 4045
Parkersburg, WV 26104 304-485-9295

Pachmayr
1875 S. Mountain Ave.
Monrovia, CA 91016 800-357-7771

Ram-Line
10601 West 48th Ave.
Wheat Ridge, CO 80401 800-648-9624

Sigarms, Inc.
Industrial Dr.
Exeter, NH 03833 603-772-2302

TJ's Custom Gunworks
P.O. Box 145
Ontario, CA 91762 714-923-4422

Tasco Sports Optics
P.O. Box 520080
Miami, FL 33152-0080 305-591-3670

Trijicon, Inc.
P. O. Box 2130
Farmington Hills, MI 48018 313-553-4960

Appendix B
Useful Publications and Videos

The following magazines are good sources of information about current trends in the firearms industry, including those of the SIG, SIG-Hammerli, and SIG-Sauer companies as well as U. S. importers of these firearms.

American Firearms Industry (Monthly magazine)
2455 E. Sunrise Blvd.
Ft. Lauderdale, FL 33304

American Rifleman (Monthly magazine)
National Rifle Association
1600 Rhode Island Ave., NW
Washington, DC 20036

Combat Handguns (Monthly magazine)
1115 Broadway
New York, NY 10010

Gun Digest (Yearly, book format)
DBI Books, Inc.
One Northfield Plaza
Northfield, IL 60093

Guns & Ammo (Monthly magazine)
P.O. Box 51214
Boulder, CO 80323-1214

SWAT (Monthly Magazine)
LFP, Inc.
9171 Wilshire Blvd., Suite 300
Beverly Hills, CA 90210

The following books are excellent sources of information about firearms and their history, including that of the SIG and SIG-Sauer guns:

Apendices

The 100 Greatest Combat Pistols
By Timothy J. Mullin
Paladin Press
P. O. Box 1307
Boulder, CO 80306-1307

Automatics
By Duncan Long
Paladin Press
P. O. Box 1307
Boulder, CO 80306-1307

Cartridges of the World
By Frank C. Barnes
4092 Commercial Ave.
Northbrook, IL 60062

Handgun Stopping Power
By Evan P Marshall and Edwin J. Sanow
Paladin Press
P. O. Box 1307
Boulder, CO 80306-1307

Military Small Arms of the 20th Century (6th Edition)
Ivan V. Hogg and John Weeks
4092 Commercial Ave.
Northbrook, IL 60062

Pistols of the World
By Ian V. Hogg and John Weeks
Presidio Press
1114 Irwin St.
San Rafael, CA 94901

The following videos are excellent sources of information about shooting techniques which can be applied to the S&W guns:

Basic Guide to Handguns
By Jeff Cooper
Mail Order Videos
7888 Ostrow St., Suite A.
San Diego, CA 92111

Bill Wilson Presents: SIG-Sauer P226 and P220
Safe-Trek Outfitters
1716 W. Main
Bozeman, MT 59715

IPSC Secrets
By Brian Enos and Lenny Magill
Mail Order Videos
7888 Ostrow St., Suite A.
San Diego, CA 92111

Pistol Masters
By Rob Leatham (with Brian Enos, J. Michael Plaxco, and others)
Mail Order Videos
7888 Ostrow St., Suite A.
San Diego, CA 92111

Secrets of Gunfighting: Israeli Style
By Eugene Sockut
Paladin Press
P. O. Box 1307

Notes

Notes